# Focus on U.S. History:

# The Era of Modernization Through the 1930s

Kathy Sammis

# User's Guide
## to
## *Walch Reproducible Books*

As part of our general effort to provide educational materials that are as practical and economical as possible, we have designated this publication a "reproducible book." The designation means that purchase of the book includes purchase of the right to limited reproduction of all pages on which this symbol appears:

Here is the basic Walch policy: We grant to individual purchasers of this book the right to make sufficient copies of reproducible pages for use by all students of a single teacher. This permission is limited to a single teacher and does not apply to entire schools or school systems, so institutions purchasing the book should pass the permission on to a single teacher. Copying of the book or its parts for resale is prohibited.

Any questions regarding this policy or requests to purchase further reproduction rights should be addressed to:

Permissions Editor
J. Weston Walch, Publisher
P. O. Box 658
Portland, Maine 04104-0658

SUSTAINABLE FORESTRY INITIATIVE

Certified Chain of Custody
Promoting Sustainable
Forest Management
www.sfiprogram.org

SGS-SFI/COC-US09/5501

1    2    3    4    5    6    7    8    9    10

ISBN 0-8251-3877-9

Copyright © 2000
J. Weston Walch, Publisher
P.O. Box 658 • Portland, Maine 04104-0658
www.walch.com

Printed in the United States of America

# CONTENTS

*Art Credits* ............................................................... *vi*

*To the Teacher* ........................................................... *vii*

*To the Student* ........................................................... *ix*

*Map: The United States* ................................................... *x*

## UNIT 1. THE PROGRESSIVE ERA

Teacher Guide ............................................................. 1

Student Background Pages ................................................. 3

*Worksheets*

    1. Death of a President ............................................... 6

    2. Reform Movements ................................................ 8

    3. Reforming Government and Politics ................................. 9

    4. Upton Sinclair, Muckraker ......................................... 11

    5. Theodore Roosevelt's New Nationalism ............................. 13

    6. Women and Work ................................................ 14

    7. Presidential Elections ............................................. 16

    8. TR Talks ......................................................... 17

    9. National Lands ................................................... 18

    10. Progressive Era Time Line......................................... 19

## UNIT 2. THE UNITED STATES AND WORLD AFFAIRS

Teacher Guide ............................................................. 21

Student Background Pages ................................................. 23

*Worksheets*

    1. The United States in Latin America ................................. 27

    2. U.S. Policy and Latin America ..................................... 28

    3. A Wartime Warning .............................................. 31

    4. Wilson's War Message ............................................ 32

    5. Don't Enter the War! ............................................. 33

    6. Enter the War: Yes or No? ......................................... 34

    7. Weapons of the War .............................................. 35

8. Life in the Trenches ................................................ 36

9. War Propaganda ................................................... 37

10. Women and the War ............................................. 39

11. Your Right to Free Speech .................................... 40

12. The League of Nations: Yes or No? ....................... 41

# UNIT 3. THE ROARING TWENTIES

Teacher Guide ............................................................ 43

Student Background Pages ........................................... 45

*Worksheets*

1. The Urban-Rural Change ...................................... 48

2. The Great Migration ............................................ 50

3. Returning African-American Soldiers .................... 51

4. African-American Life in the North ....................... 52

5. Immigration Ups and Downs ................................. 53

6. Reading the Immigration Graph ............................ 54

7. The "New Woman" .............................................. 55

8. Women and Work, 1920s Style .............................. 56

9. The Great American Game .................................... 57

10. Twenties Talk ..................................................... 58

11. Sports Stars ....................................................... 59

12. The Automobile and the American Landscape .......... 60

# UNIT 4. THE GREAT DEPRESSION

Teacher Guide ............................................................ 61

Student Background Pages ........................................... 63

*Worksheets*

1. Your Economic Problems ...................................... 66

2. Presidential Elections: 1928 and 1932 ................... 67

3. Your Stock Market Losses .................................... 68

4. Hooverisms ........................................................ 69

5. Images of the Great Depression ............................ 70

6. The Life of Tenant Farmers .................................. 72

7. The Great Depression at Home .............................. 73

8. Women of the Thirties: In Real Life ....................... 74

9. Women of the Thirties: On the Screen .................... 75

# UNIT 5. THE NEW DEAL

Teacher Guide ............................................................................ 77

Student Background Pages ........................................................ 79

*Worksheets*

    1. Hoover vs. Roosevelt ..................................................... 82

    2. Presidential Campaigns, 1900–1932 ............................. 85

    3. TR and FDR ................................................................ 86

    4. What Is It? A New Deal Game ..................................... 87

    5. You and the New Deal .................................................. 90

    6. Be a New Deal Worker ................................................. 91

    7. Share Our Wealth ........................................................ 92

    8. No New Deal! ............................................................... 93

    9. The Supreme Court and the New Deal ........................ 94

  10. FDR and the Supreme Court ....................................... 95

  11. The New Deal Time Line ............................................. 96


*Answers, Additional Activities, and Assessments* ........................... 97

*Additional Resources* ..................................................... 113

*Glossary* ................................................................ 115

# ART CREDITS

# TO THE TEACHER

The beginning of the twentieth century saw the growth of the Progressive reform movement and the emergence of modern America. A corrosive set of problems had developed in the second half of the nineteenth century, as the country had experienced great growth in industry, cities, and immigration while at the same time business and political leaders became increasingly corrupt. In the first two decades of the twentieth century, a group of mostly white, middle-class, and often female reformers attacked these myriad problems with determination and a great deal of success.

Meanwhile, the early twentieth century saw the United States enter more fully into its role as a world leader, a role that had started with the U.S. victory in the 1898 Spanish-American War. The United States became deeply involved in Latin America under presidents Roosevelt, Taft, and Wilson, and it continued to work to protect its economic interests in the Far East.

After attempting to remain neutral, the United States was finally drawn into World War I. In the aftermath of the war, the country once again turned its back on foreign affairs and concentrated on the vibrant economy and culture of the 1920s, which also saw the spread of anti-immigrant and anti-minority reactions.

The stock market crash of 1929 ended the Roaring Twenties with a bang and ushered in the very difficult and demoralizing years of the Great Depression. Franklin Roosevelt's New Deal attacked the Depression and in the process transformed the role of government in Americans' lives, initiating the modern welfare state.

The reproducible student activities in this book draw students into this era of modern change, helping them develop a rich understanding of these events that have so affected contemporary times. Many activities in this book use original source materials; these materials make the experiences and thoughts of the people who lived in and shaped what may seem like a remote era more immediate and accessible to students. Primary source materials help students enter into these events and experience them, feel the ways in which actual people experienced and affected their contemporary life that has become history.

## Organization

The student activity topics are divided into units guided by the National Standards for History. Each unit begins with several Student Background Pages that give the most relevant information on that unit's topic. A number of reproducible student activity pages follow, including reading selections from original contemporary sources and a variety of activities: decision-making, comprehension, analytical, comparative, chronological, interpretive, research, mapping and graphing, role-playing, interactive, and interdisciplinary.

Each unit includes some Extra Challenge activities to provide enrichment for more advanced or adventurous students. Time-line activities remind students of chronology, while inviting them into wider descriptive and illustrative areas. A map of the United States is provided; you can make copies as needed for applicable activities.

Each unit is preceded by a Teacher Guide, giving you an overview of the unit and its objectives, plus specific teaching information on each student activity.

Lower-level students may have some difficulty reading some of the original source documents, as they contain some formal and higher-level words and syntax. You might want to go over some or all original source selections in class to be sure all students understand them fully.

At the back of this book, you'll find a section titled Answers, Additional Activities, and Assessments. Answers for the student activities, a list of suggested additional activities, and several assessment vehicles have been provided for each unit. The resource section gives titles of fiction and nonfiction books that will enrich students' learning and be helpful to you, plus media/computer research and enrichment resources. The glossary is reproducible for students' use.

# To the Student

The United States became a modern society in the first 30 years of the twentieth century. A group of reformers called Progressives attacked a set of nasty problems. Cities and industries had grown a lot. Living and working conditions were getting worse. Many business and political leaders were corrupt. Progressive reformers wrote and spoke about these problems. They got many reform laws passed. Some laws cleaned up politics. Others forbade unfair and corrupt ways of doing business. New reform laws also protected workers and helped urban dwellers and poor people. Women got the right to vote at last. Minorities, however, didn't gain much during the Progressive era.

Meanwhile, the United States was becoming a world leader. It kept trade in China open to all nations. It got an agreement with Japan to end Japanese immigration into the United States. It became very active in the Caribbean area and Central America. The United States often interfered with the domestic affairs of Latin American nations between 1900 and 1930. When World War I broke out in Europe, the United States tried to stay out of the fighting. But it was finally drawn into that conflict in 1917.

After the war, life was good for many Americans. The economy boomed. A lively mass culture arose. Young people created their own youth-centered culture. Women had fewer limits on their lives. African Americans moved North in great numbers. Black arts flourished during the Harlem Renaissance. But anti-immigrant and anti-minority tensions were a dark side to the 1920s.

The boom times ended abruptly in 1929. The stock market crashed, and the Great Depression began. Millions of Americans had no jobs, some for years. People lost their homes, their life savings. Farms, businesses, and banks collapsed. Things just kept getting worse until Franklin D. Roosevelt became president early in 1933. He launched a set of programs called the New Deal. New laws regulated business and farming. Unemployed people got federal jobs. The U.S. government provided social services for those who needed them. The era of government as a part of most people's lives had begun.

The activities you'll be doing for this course of study will help you better understand this era of modern change. You'll work with maps and graphs. You'll put yourself into the shoes of people of these times. You'll decide what New Deal job to apply for, or whether to risk the threat of German submarine attacks on a sea voyage. You'll debate the questions of entering World War I and jobs for women. You'll describe your struggles to cope with the Great Depression. You'll also read what people of this era said when they spoke out about the great issues of the times. You'll hear what soldiers, tenant farmers, and a U.S. president had to say about their experiences. When you're done, you'll have a better grasp of these years of dramatic change for the United States.

Name _____   Date _____

# United States

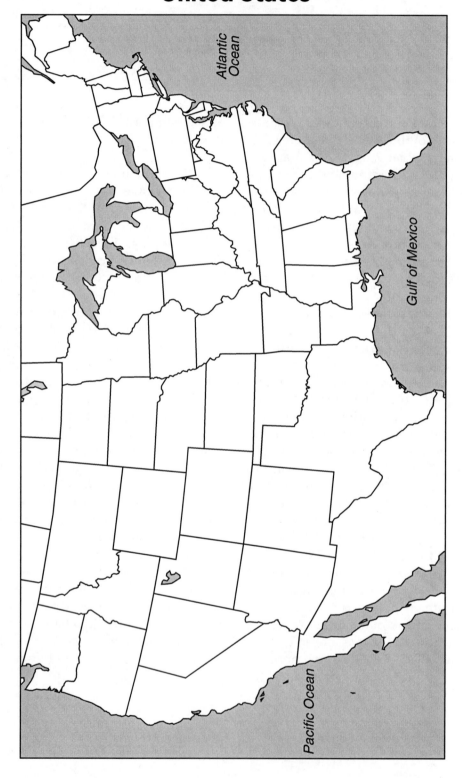

x

*Focus on U.S. History:*
*The Era of Modernization Through the 1930s*

# The Progressive Era

The objective of this unit is to help students understand the ways in which the Progressive movement and Progressive reformers addressed the political, social, and economic problems in the United States in the early twentieth century. These problems had developed in the decades after the Civil War, and reforms of the late 1800s had only begun to tackle them. Progressive reformers set out to fix problems at the local, state, and national levels. They cleaned up corrupt, machine-dominated local and state politics. They worked for laws to regulate big business and protect workers and consumers. They developed programs to help assimilate the ongoing influx of immigrants. They inspired four constitutional amendments—income tax, direct election of sena-

tors, prohibition, and women's suffrage. Progressivism became part of national politics with reform-minded presidents Theodore Roosevelt, Woodrow Wilson, and, to a lesser extent, William H. Taft. Roosevelt firmly established conservation and wilderness preservation as national policy.

Progressivism had its limitations, however. Its primary proponents showed little interest in African Americans and other minorities, were antagonistic to radical labor movements, and limited their interest in women's rights almost entirely to suffrage. This unit's activities are designed to draw students into a better understanding of the many elements of the Progressive era.

# Student Activities

**Death of a President** gives students a dramatic description of the shooting of President McKinley in September 1901. Students are invited to follow the events of the following week via contemporary news accounts or investigate other notable U.S. assassinations.

**Reform Movements** provides a frame for students to identify elements of various Progressive-era reform movements.

**Reforming Government and Politics** has students identify important political reforms that Progressives achieved and explain why each improved government and politics.

**Upton Sinclair, Muckraker,** presents excerpts from Sinclair's 1906 novel *The Jungle* that describe the unsanitary conditions in Chicago's meat-packing industry and the reliance of the poor on adulterated

food and medicine. Students are asked to identify and learn more about the reforms that Congress passed in response to Sinclair's writing. The Extra Challenge asks students to find a current muckraking article and share it with classmates.

**Theodore Roosevelt's New Nationalism** presents portions of a 1910 speech in which Roosevelt described an element of his New Nationalism that is still a very current topic—reform of campaign financing and the role of special interests and corporations in politics. Students research today's debate on these questions and evaluate current reform proposals as well as Roosevelt's suggestions.

**Women and Work** presents the arguments made against women working outside the home as expressed in a 1901 periodical article. Students identify the main points made by the article's writer and then develop a rebuttal to each of the objections, writing as commentators of either the early twentieth century or today. Their rebuttals are framed as either a periodical article or radio/TV commentary. The Extra Challenge asks students to role-play a debate among supporters and opponents of working women in the early twentieth century.

**Presidential Elections** presents the results of the 1912 and 1916 presidential elections. From this, students create sets of pie charts and contrasting state-by-state election maps and compare these sets by year. The Challenge Question asks students to consider how results of the 1912 election might have been different if Theodore Roosevelt had not run as the candidate of a third party.

**TR Talks** personalizes the always interesting Theodore Roosevelt by presenting some of

Roosevelt's colorful and revealing comments. Students take turns explaining what Roosevelt is referring to in each comment.

**National Lands** introduces students to the policy established by President Roosevelt of setting aside land in many parts of the country for national parks, monuments, and wildlife preserves. Students locate and label the listed national lands (protected between 1872 and 1910) on their map of the United States.

**Progressive Era Time Line** lists significant milestones in the Progressive era and asks students to create a time line with dates and descriptions of the events.

Name _____

Date _____

# The Progressive Era

## *Progressives and Progressivism*

The last third of the nineteenth century had been a period of great growth in the United States. It was an era of big business and big industry. Politics were corrupt. Monopolies kept prices high and exploited workers. Immigrants and other workers crowded into packed cities. Poor urban dwellers needed many social services. But city governments were not able to provide these services. Some reforms to fix these problems were passed in the late 1800s. But much remained to be done.

A new movement grew across the nation in the early 1900s. It was called **Progressivism**. Progressives wanted the reforms of the late 1800s to continue and expand. They wanted to make people's lives better. They denounced corporate greed.

## *The Muckrakers*

Most Progressives were members of the middle class. They were also mostly well-educated. Some were journalists. That is, they wrote articles for newspapers and magazines. These reform-minded writers began looking into and writing about specific problems. (This is called "investigative journalism." It's still very popular today, in all types of media.)

**Nellie Bly**

President Theodore Roosevelt didn't like these writers. He said they were like the man with the muckrake in an old Christian book. The man raked up all the filth of society but didn't see the good. Roosevelt's comment gave the crusading writers their famous nickname: **muckrakers**. The muckrakers had a great impact on public opinion.

◆ Ida Tarbell exposed Rockefeller's Standard Oil Company in McClure's in 1902.

◆ Lincoln Steffens exposed local political corruption in "Shame of the Cities" in 1904.

◆ Nellie Bly had herself committed to a mental hospital to expose shocking treatment there.

**Upton Sinclair** published a widely read novel titled *The Jungle* in 1906. In it, Sinclair sickened Americans with his graphic and stomach-turning descriptions of the conditions in Chicago's meat-packing houses. Within that same year, Congress passed the Meat Inspection Act and the Pure Food and Drug Act.

*(continued)*

# The Progressive Era *(continued)*

## Progressive Reforms

The Progressive movement made many reforms. Progressives took over and cleaned up many city governments. They broke the power of state political machines as well. Wisconsin led the way. Governor Robert La Follette was a Progressive. He directed a sweeping set of reforms called the "Wisconsin idea." Some laws checked campaign finances and lobbying. Others set up direct primary votes. Groups of experts were formed to help run the state. Other states soon adopted these reforms, too.

Progressives also pushed through state social reforms. Children younger than a stated age could not have jobs. Limits were set on working hours for women and children. Laws mandated job safety and minimum wages.

In the late 1800s, Jane Addams spearheaded the **settlement house** movement. Her Hull House in Chicago was a community center. It offered immigrants and poor workers who lived nearby a wide range of services. Clients of a settlement house could get English lessons, cooking and nutrition lessons, child care, sports activities, and much more.

**Jane Addams**

## Progressive Presidents

The Progressive era at the White House started with a tragedy. President William McKinley was shot to death in 1901. Progressive Vice President Theodore Roosevelt suddenly became president. Roosevelt said he would give the American people a **"Square Deal."** The government would stop unfair ways of doing business.

McKinley adviser Mark Hanna hadn't wanted Roosevelt on the ticket in 1900. When McKinley died, Hanna exlaimed, "Now look—that damned cowboy is president of the United States!"

**Theodore Roosevelt**

Roosevelt did as he promised. He broke up trusts. He got big businesses to accept more federal rules. He forced mine owners to come to terms with striking coal miners in 1902. He had a great love of the outdoors. So he made conservation of natural resources a key federal policy. As president, he set aside 150 million acres of land. They became national parks, forests, monuments, and wildlife preserves.

William Howard Taft became president in 1908. He kept some Progressive reform going. But his lack of good political sense cost him friends. One of these was Roosevelt. TR decided he wanted to take back the reins in 1912. The Republicans chose Taft to run for president that year, though. So Roosevelt ran as head of the new Progressive party. This split Republican voters. The Democrats' candidate won by a wide margin.

When the Progressive party nominated him, TR declared, "I'm feeling like a bull moose!" His party instantly became known as the Bull Moose party.

*(continued)*

# The Progressive Era (continued)

The new Democratic president was Woodrow Wilson. He was also a Progressive. He called his federal reform program the "**New Freedom.**" Wilson got Congress to lower tariffs. This helped farmers and consumers. He also got a law passed to set up a national banking system. Other laws put brakes on unfair ways of doing business.

## The Progressive Amendments

Four amendments to the U.S. Constitution were passed during the Progressive era. The Sixteenth and Seventeenth Amendments were both ratified in 1913. The Sixteenth Amendment allowed a federal income tax. The Sixteenth mandated direct election of U.S. senators. The Eighteenth Amendment was ratified in 1919. It forbade making or selling alcoholic beverages. The Nineteenth Amendment, ratified in 1920, ended a long struggle. It gave American women the vote.

## The Limitations of Progressivism

Progressives favored all kinds of reform. But they did have their blind and prejudiced sides. Many, but not all, Progressives favored women's suffrage. (A common idea was that women had "refined sensibilities." Therefore, they would "purify" politics.) But, the Progressive movement had little interest in any other questions of equal rights for women.

African Americans and other minorities were largely left out of this reform movement.

Some things even got worse. Black rights in the South eroded further. President Wilson segregated federal workers. More and more, African Americans responded to leaders like W. E. B. DuBois. He urged his fellow blacks to be proud of their color and their African background.

> Theodore Roosevelt expressed a common view of women's rights in 1910: "We hear much about women's rights. Well, as to that, decent men should be thinking about women's rights all the time, and while the men are doing that—the women should be attending to their duties."

Native Americans did not make gains during the Progressive era either. Most Progressives viewed Indians as second-class citizens destined to remain that way. This second-class view also applied to immigrants. Large numbers of people were coming to the United States from Asia. Many more were immigrating from southern and eastern Europe. Narrow-minded nativists were alarmed. So were many middle-class reformers.

Some workers didn't think Progressive reforms went far enough. They turned to more radical answers. The Industrial Workers of the World (IWW) was founded in 1905. The IWW wanted to end capitalism. Workers around the world would unite and take over the means of production. Other people who favored more radical politics turned to the Socialist party. It called for government ownership of businesses and industries. This would give the people more control.

> Eugene V. Debs was the Socialist candidate for U.S. president five times. In his first run in 1900, he polled fewer than 100,000 votes. In his last run in 1920, he got over 900,000 votes—even though he was in jail at the time for speaking out against the World War I draft.

5

*Focus on U.S. History:*
*The Era of Modernization Through the 1930s*

# Death of a President

On September 6, 1901, an assassin shot President William McKinley at the Pan-American Exposition in Buffalo, New York. Here is part of a news account describing the shooting.

---

### *The New York Times,* September 6, 1901

A vast crowd had assembled long before the arrival of Mr. McKinley. . . . The President, though well guarded by United States Secret Service detectives, was fully exposed to such an attack as occurred. He stood at the edge of the raised dais, and throngs of people crowded in at the various entrances to see their Chief Executive, perchance to clasp his hand, and then fight their way out in the good-natured mob that every minute swelled and multiplied at the points of ingress and egress to the building.

The President was in a cheerful mood and was enjoying the hearty evidences of good-will which everywhere met his gaze. . . .

It was shortly after 4 o'clock when one of the throng which surrounded the Presidential party, a medium-sized man of ordinary appearance and plainly dressed in black, approached as if to greet the President. . . . President McKinley smiled, bowed, and extended his hand in that spirit of geniality the American people so well know, when suddenly the man raised his hand and two sharp reports of a revolver rang out loud and clear above the hum of voices and the shuffling of myriad feet. . . .

There was an instant of almost complete silence, like the hush that follows a clap of thunder. The President stood stock still, a look of hesitancy, almost of bewilderment,

on his face. Then he retreated a step while a pallor began to steal over his features. . . .

Then came a commotion. With the leap of a tiger three men threw themselves forward as with one impulse and sprang toward the would-be assassin. . . . In a twinkling the assassin was borne to the ground, his weapon was wrested from his grasp, and strong arms pinioned him down.

Then the vast multitude which thronged the edifice began to come to a realizing sense of the awfulness of the scene of which they had been witnesses. A murmur arose, spread, and swelled to a hum of confusion, then grew to a babel of sounds, and later to a pandemonium of noises. . . .

Inside on the slightly raised dais was enacted within those few feverish moments a tragedy, so dramatic in character, so thrilling in its intensity, that few who looked on will ever be able to give a succinct account of what really did transpire. Even the actors who were playing the principal roles came out of it with blanched faces, trembling limbs, and beating hearts, while their brains throbbed with a tumult of conflicting emotions which left behind only a chaotic jumble of impressions which could not be clarified into a lucid narrative of the events as they really transpired.

---

*(continued)*

# Death of a President *(continued)*

**Directions:** Complete one or more of the following exercises.

1. For eight days, the nation hung on newspaper accounts of McKinley's fight for life—and the search for Vice President Roosevelt, off on a wilderness hunting trip. On microfilm or on the Internet, follow the story of President McKinley's shooting through at least September 14, when he died and Theodore Roosevelt became president. Make copies of newspaper head-lines and stories. Then create a bulletin board or poster display so other students can follow the drama themselves.

2. Find newspaper accounts of other assassinations of U.S. presidents or public figures.

    (a) Create a display or audiovisual presentation of one of these other assassinations.

    (b) Write your own newspaper account of one of these other assassinations in the style of the 1901 McKinley story—that is, use a more colorful and less impartial style than modern newspapers do. You could underline the colorful and emotional words and phrases in the McKinley account to give yourself a stylistic guide.

    (c) Write your own first-person eyewitness account of one of these assassinations. (Look at photographs and film/video footage in addition to reading newspaper accounts to get details for your personal narrative.)

**President McKinley**

*Focus on U.S. History:
The Era of Modernization Through the 1930s*

# Reform Movements

The Progressive era featured many reform movements. Some were associated with the Progressives. Others went beyond Progressivism to promote more radical reforms or to represent minorities whom the Progressives mostly ignored. For a handy summary of important reform movements, fill in the chart below.

| Movement | Main issue or concern | Main reform organization(s) | Major leader(s) | Main accomplishment(s), 1900–1920 |
|---|---|---|---|---|
| temperance | | | | |
| child labor | | | | |
| socialism | | | | |
| women's suffrage | | | | |
| radical labor | | | | |
| black rights | | | | |
| anarchism | | | | |

Name _____

Date _____

# Reforming Government and Politics

Reforms in government and politics, at both the national and the state level, were a major goal of the Progressive movement. Listed below are some important reforms that helped achieve this goal. They are still a part of government and politics today. Explain what each one is and why reformers thought it was an improvement.

**1. initiative**

What: _____

_____

Improvement: _____

_____

**2. recall**

What: _____

_____

Improvement: _____

_____

**3. referendum**

What: _____

_____

Improvement: _____

_____

**4. citywide elections**

What: _____

_____

Improvement: _____

_____

*(continued)*

Name ______________________________

Date ______________________________

UNIT 1
WORKSHEET 3

# Reforming Government and Politics *(continued)*

5. **secret ballot**

   What: ______________________________

   ______________________________

   Improvement: ______________________________

   ______________________________

6. **direct primary**

   What: ______________________________

   ______________________________

   Improvement: ______________________________

   ______________________________

7. **city manager**

   What: ______________________________

   ______________________________

   Improvement: ______________________________

   ______________________________

8. **"gas and water socialism"**

   What: ______________________________

   ______________________________

   Improvement: ______________________________

   ______________________________

# Upton Sinclair, Muckraker

Journalists in the Progressive era often wrote about corrupt politics and dishonest ways of doing business. These writers were called **muckrakers**. They raked up dirt and exposed it to public view. Upton Sinclair was a socialist and a muckraker. In 1906, he published a novel titled *The Jungle*. Sinclair's main purpose in the novel was to expose the misdeeds of big business and politicians. He showed the brutal ways they exploited and put down working-class people. Some sections of the novel were very graphic. They described in great detail the shocking, unclean practices of Chicago's meat-packing industry. Here's one of those passages.

. . . There was never the least attention paid to what was cut up for sausage; there would come all the way back from Europe old sausage that had been rejected, and that was moldy and white—it would be dosed with borax and glycerine, and dumped into the hoppers, and made over again for home consumption. There would be meat that had tumbled out on the floor, in the dirt and sawdust, where the workers had tramped and spit uncounted billions of consumption [tuberculosis] germs. There would be meat stored in great piles in rooms; and the water from leaky roofs would drip over it, and thousands of rats would race about on it. It was too dark in these storage places to see well, but a man could run his hand over these piles of meat and sweep off handfuls of the dried dung of rats. These rats were nuisances, and the packers would put poisoned bread out for them; they would die, and then rats, bread, and meat would go into the hoppers together. This is no fairy story and no joke; the meat would be shoveled into carts, and the man who did the shoveling would not trouble to lift out a rat even when he saw one—there were things that went into the sausage in comparison with which a poisoned rat was a tidbit.

There was no place for the men to wash their hands before they ate their dinner, and so they made a practice of washing them in the water that was to be ladled into the sausage. There were the butt-ends of smoked meat, and the scraps of corned beef, and all the odds and ends of the waste of the plants, that would be dumped into old barrels in the cellar and left there. Under the system of rigid economy which the packers enforced, there were some jobs that it only paid to do once in a long time, and among these was the cleaning out of the waste barrels. Every spring they did it; and in the barrels would be dirt and rust and old nails and stale water—and cartload after cartload of it would be taken up and dumped into the hoppers with fresh meat, and sent out to the public's breakfast. . . .

All of their sausage came out of the same bowl, but when they came to wrap it they would stamp some of it "special," and for this they would charge two cents more a pound.

*(continued)*

# Upton Sinclair, Muckraker *(continued)*

Here's another passage from *The Jungle* about the foods and medicines sold to poor people.

Their [the immigrants'] children were not as well as they had been at home [back in Europe]; but how . . . could they know that the pale-blue milk that they bought around the corner was watered, and doctored with formaldehyde besides? When the children were not well at home, Teta Elzbieta would gather herbs and cure them; now she was obliged to go to the drugstore and buy extracts—and how was she to know that they were all adulterated? How could they find out that their tea and coffee, their sugar and flour, had been doctored; that their canned peas had been colored with copper salts, and their fruit jams with aniline dyes? And even if they had known it, what good would it have done them, since there was no place within miles of them where any other sort was to be had?

**Directions:** First, answer these questions about what you have just read.

1. What law did Congress pass in 1906 to fix the problems Sinclair describes in the meat-packing industry?

   _____

2. What law did Congress pass in 1906 to regulate the problems with foods and medicines that Sinclair describes?

   _____

Now, research and report on regulations today that govern meat-processing or food and drug ingredients and labeling.

**Extra Challenge:** Find a muckraking article in a current newspaper or magazine, or on the Internet. Bring a copy of it to class to share with fellow students.

# Theodore Roosevelt's New Nationalism

Theodore Roosevelt ran for president in 1912 calling for a policy he dubbed "New Nationalism." Under "New Nationalism," the federal government would put "national need before sectional or personal advantage." It would act as an agent of reform for the public welfare. Here are parts of Roosevelt's speech at Osawatomie, Kansas, outlining his "New Nationalism" program.

---

**Theodore Roosevelt, 1910**

. . . Our government, national and state, must be freed from the sinister influence or control of special interests. . . . We must drive the special interests out of politics.

. . . There can be no effective control of corporations while their political activity remains. To put an end to it will be neither a short nor an easy task, but it can be done.

. . . It is necessary that laws should be passed to prohibit the use of corporate funds directly or indirectly for political purposes; it is still more necessary that such laws should be thoroughly enforced.

. . . One of the fundamental necessities in a representative government such as ours is to make certain that the men to whom the people delegate their power shall serve the people by whom they are elected and not the special interests. I believe that every national officer, elected or appointed, should be forbidden to perform any service or receive any compensation, directly or indirectly, from interstate corporations; and a similar provision could not fail to be useful within the states.

---

**Directions:** Research and read about today's debate on the role of special interests and corporations in politics. Then discuss in class Roosevelt's proposals, as well as current proposals, "to prohibit the use of corporate funds directly or indirectly for political purposes" and to make it illegal for government officials "to perform any service or receive any compensation, directly or indirectly, from . . . corporations."

You could discuss questions such as these: What abuses are these proposals intended to check? How might these proposals change the modern political system? Do you think these proposals would be effective? What solution would you suggest to control the power of corporations and special interests in politics?

# Women and Work

By the beginning of the twentieth century, many more women were working at paid jobs outside the home than ever before. This trend alarmed many people. Here is a sample of the standard reasons given to explain why women should stay at home unless absolutely necessary.

---

**Henry T. Finck, writing in *The Independent*, 1901**

. . . Instead of being encouraged in the tendency to leave the refining atmosphere of home, girls should be taught that, except under the stress of poverty, it is selfish as well as suicidal on their part to go out and work. Selfish because they take away the work which poor women and men absolutely need for their daily bread; suicidal because, by offering themselves so cheaply to employers, they either drive out the men or, by lowering their [the men's] wages from the family standard to the individual standard, make it impossible for them [the men] to marry; wherefore these same girls who had hoped by thus going out to work to increase their marriage chances, are left to die as old maids, or "new women," as they now prefer to call themselves.

Had they remained at home and cultivated the graces and refined allurements of femininity, their chances for a good marriage and a happy life would have been much better. Men still prefer, and always will prefer, the home girl to any other kind. They want a girl who has not marred her beauty and ruined her health by needless work, or rubbed off the peach bloom of innocence by exposure to a rough world.

. . . Chastity is the most womanly of all virtues, and everything that endangers it should be promptly suppressed. Factory work does this [endangers chastity] preeminently.

. . . Nervous collapse is . . . the fate of most women who engage with men in the strenuous competition of mercantile life. . . . A considerable proportion of working women are everywhere doomed to bad health.

. . . Whatever tends to unsex women should be frowned on by public opinion and, if necessary, prohibited by law. . . . All employments which make women bold, fierce, muscular, brawny in body or mind will be more and more rigidly tabooed as unwomanly. Woman's strength lies in beauty and gentleness, not in muscle.

. . . Let us by all means throw open to [women] all employments in which their health, their purity, and their womanliness do not suffer; but let this be regarded, not as a special privilege and an indication of social progress, but as a necessary evil to be cured in as many cases as possible by marriage or some other way of bringing the workers back to their deserted homes.

---

*(continued)*

# Women and Work *(continued)*

**Directions:** Why should women **not** take paid jobs outside the home, according to Finck? List the reasons Finck states on the lines below.

1. harm caused to others:_____

   _____

2. damage to marriage prospects:_____

   _____

3. moral harm:_____

   _____

4. health harm: _____

   _____

5. harm to "womanliness":_____

   _____

Now, develop a rebuttal to each of these objections, appropriate for the early twentieth century or for today. Frame your rebuttal as an article for a newspaper or magazine, or as a radio or TV commentary. Be sure to rebut each point Finck makes.

"For women to work is a sin."
"The world would be better off if all women were turned out of their jobs tomorrow."
—Reverend S. G. Smith, sociologist, c. 1900

**Extra Challenge:** Role-play a debate among supporters and opponents of working women in the early twentieth century.

Working women, c. 1900–1910

# Presidential Elections

**Directions:** Listed below are the results of the 1912 and the 1916 presidential elections. Use this information to complete the exercises below the chart.

| Year | Candidate | Party | Popular Vote | Electoral Vote |
|------|-----------|-------|--------------|----------------|
| **1912** | Woodrow Wilson | Democratic | 6,286,820 | 435 |
| | Theodore Roosevelt | Progressive | 4,126,020 | 88 |
| | William H. Taft | Republican | 3,483,922 | 8 |
| | Eugene V. Debs | Socialist | 900,672 | - - - |
| | Eugene W. Chafin | Prohibition | 206,275 | - - - |
| **1916** | Woodrow Wilson | Democratic | 9,129,606 | 277 |
| | Charles E. Hughes | Republican | 8,538,221 | 254 |
| | A.L. Benson | Socialist | 585,113 | - - - |
| | J. Frank Hanly | Prohibition | 220,506 | - - - |

1. From the figures above, create for each election **two sets of pie charts** showing (a) popular support and (b) electoral vote for each party's candidates. **Calculate the percentage** of the total each candidate won in each vote, and show this on your pie charts.

2. On your map of the United States, show which states each candidate won. Consult your text, an encyclopedia, or the Internet to find the state-by-state results.

3. Compare the pie charts. How did electoral vote percentages compare with popular vote percentages? What do the 1912 results tell you about popular support for reforms? How were results in 1916 different from results in 1912?

4. Compare the maps. How did Wilson's state-by-state results change between 1912 and 1916?

> **Challenge Question:** How might results of the 1912 election have been different if Theodore Roosevelt had not split off from the Republican party to run as the Progressive party candidate?

# TR Talks

**Directions:** Theodore Roosevelt was a colorful, energetic, and outspoken man. Below are some quotations from TR. As your teacher reads each quote aloud, you and your classmates will take turns explaining what Roosevelt is referring to in each comment.

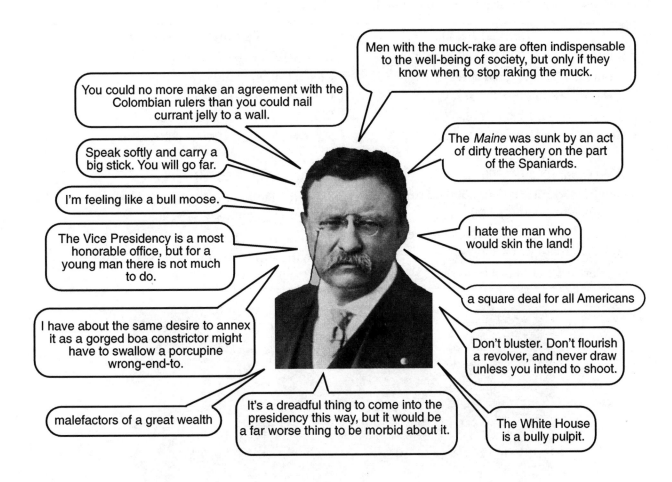

# National Lands

Theodore Roosevelt believed deeply in conservation of U.S. lands. So, the early years of the 1900s saw the establishment of many national parks, monuments, and wildlife preserves. (Several national parks had been established in the late 1800s, too.) Listed below are some of these national parks, monuments, and wildlife preserves. (The list includes the date each one was established. The list also gives the approximate area of each park and monument.)

**Directions:** Locate and label these national lands on your map of the United States.

| National Parks | National Monuments |
|---|---|
| Yellowstone, 1872 (2,220,000 acres) | Devil's Tower, 1906 (1,350 acres) |
| Sequoia, 1890 (402,500 acres) | Chaco Canyon, 1907 (34,000 acres) |
| Yosemite, 1890 (760,000 acres) | Pinnacles, 1908 (16,200 acres) |
| Grand Canyon, 1893 (1,218,400 acres) | Muir Woods, 1908 (550 acres) |
| Mount Rainier, 1899 (235,400 acres) | Natural Bridges, 1908 (7,800 acres) |
| Crater Lake, 1902 (183,000 acres) | |
| Wind Cave, 1903 (28,300 acres) | **Wildlife Preserves** |
| Petrified Forest, 1906 (93,500 acres) | Pelican Island, 1903 |
| Mesa Verde, 1906 (52,000 acres) | Wichita Game Preserves, 1905 |
| Lassen Volcanic, 1907 (106,000 acres) | National Bison Range, 1908 |
| Olympic, 1909 (914,600 acres) | Klamath and Malheur Preserves, 1908 |
| Glacier, 1910 (1,000,000+ acres) | |

Yosemite National Park

# Progressive Era Time Line

**Directions:** With classmates, construct a time line for these important milestones in the Progressive era. Include a brief description of each. Illustrations would make your time line more interesting. (Hint: The items are listed in year-by-year order.)

- NAWSA is founded
- Initiative and referendum system adopted in South Dakota
- Robert La Follette elected governor of Wisconsin
- Eugene Debs runs for president on Socialist ticket
- Direct primaries held in Minnesota
- Theodore Roosevelt becomes president
- Tarbell and Steffens articles appear in *McClure's*
- National coal strike
- Initiative system adopted in Oregon
- Dead Indian Land Act, Reclamation Act
- W. E. B. DuBois's *The Souls of Black Folk* is published
- Elkins Railroad Act
- Direct primary enacted in Wisconsin
- Department of Commerce and Labor is established
- Northern Securities case
- National Child Labor Committee is established
- Theodore Roosevelt is elected
- IWW is founded
- *Lochner* v. *New York*
- Upton Sinclair's *The Jungle* is published
- Meat Inspection Act, Pure Food and Drug Act, Hepburn Act
- Panic of 1907
- Taft is elected president
- *Muller* v. *Oregon*
- NAACP is founded
- Mann Act
- Ballinger-Pinchot affair
- Children's Bureau for Department of Labor is established
- Woodrow Wilson is elected president, Roosevelt runs as Progressive candidate
- Sixteenth and Seventeenth Amendments ratified
- Underwood Tariff Act, Federal Reserve Act
- Congressional Union is established
- Federal Trade Commission Act, Clayton Antitrust Act
- Keating-Owen Child Labor Act
- Eighteenth Amendment ratified
- Nineteenth Amendment ratified

# The United States and World Affairs

The objective of this unit is to help students understand the changing role of the United States in world affairs from 1900 through World War I. The United States began to play a leading role on the world stage when the outcome of the Spanish-American War made it an imperial power. Strong economic interests drew the United States into a role in the Far East, with the Open Door policy, Roosevelt's involvement in the resolution of the Russo-Japanese War, and the Gentlemen's Agreement of 1907–08 halting Japanese immigration into this country. The United States played a very active role in the Caribbean in the early twentieth century under Theodore Roosevelt's Big Stick policy, Taft's

Dollar Diplomacy, and Wilson's Missionary Diplomacy. Following a policy established during the presidency of George Washington, the United States worked at staying out of the war that erupted in Europe in 1914. Events finally drew the nation into that conflict in 1917. The war effort at home had a great impact on U.S. civilians. The fight between President Wilson and Senate Republicans over the League of Nations was intense and became a nationwide debate. This unit's activities are designed to draw students into a better understanding of this newly developing involvement of the United States in world affairs.

# Student Activities

**The United States in Latin America** uses mapping to familiarize students with nations in the Caribbean and Central America that experienced various levels of U.S. intervention in the early decades of the twentieth century. The Extra Challenge asks students to briefly outline the steps of various U.S. involvements in Latin American countries.

**U.S. Policy and Latin America** presents statements of policy from four different U.S. presidents, from Theodore Roosevelt to Franklin Roosevelt, and a fifth president's secretary of state. Students answer questions about the policy statements to identify the elements of each president's policy and the differences and similarities among the policies. The Extra Challenge presents a statement of Latin American policy from President Coolidge and asks students which U.S. policy toward Latin America the statement follows.

**A Wartime Warning** presents an advertisement for the sailings of the *Lusitania* in May 1915 with the warning notice about war zones and attacks on ships published in U.S. newspapers in 1915 by the German embassy. Students role-play a family discussion about whether or not to change family plans to travel to Europe aboard the *Lusitania.*

**Wilson's War Message** presents the president's message to Congress of April 2, 1917, asking for a declaration of war against Germany and giving his reasons why the United States finally was being compelled to enter the conflict. A companion worksheet follows, **Don't Enter the War!**, presenting the arguments of U.S. Senator Norris against entering the war. **Enter the War: Yes or No?** guides students through an evaluation of Wilson's and Norris's arguments via a series of questions. Students complete their evaluation in a discussion, debate, or opinion paper.

**Weapons of the War** shows some of the new, more destructive weapons of World War I. Students identify each weapon and tell how each helped to make this such a destructive war.

**Life in the Trenches** presents a World War I soldier's description of some of the miserable elements of life in the war's front-line trenches. Students then imagine themselves in those trenches and write a series of diary entries or letters home about their experiences.

**War Propaganda** shows some of the ubiquitous posters that promoted various war aims at home. Students analyze the war aim each poster promotes and the emotional appeal, symbols, and/or slogans the poster uses to get its message across.

**Women and the War** gives students a look at some female war workers performing jobs only men had filled before the war. Students use the photos as a catalyst to imagine themselves in the place of a young woman working a wartime job and earning her own living for the first time.

**Your Right to Free Speech** presents part of the Espionage and Sedition Act of 1918 and then asks students to identify which of a list of nine specific actions would have gotten them arrested under the provisions of the 1917 and 1918 acts. Students will probably be surprised to discover that all of the listed actions got actual people arrested, including criticizing the YMCA and President Wilson's foreign policy toward Mexico.

**The League of Nations: Yes or No?** presents statements by President Wilson in favor of the United States joining the League of Nations and by U.S. Senator Borah opposing U.S. entry into the League. Students read some more opinions on both sides of this issue and then role-play a debate between people on the two sides.

# The United States and World Affairs

The Spanish-American War of 1898 made the United States an imperial power. It now controlled Puerto Rico in the Caribbean and the Philippines in the Pacific Ocean. It also had the right to intervene in newly independent Cuba. During the first 20 years of the twentieth century, the United States fully stepped into its new role as a leading world power.

## Involvement in Asia

Many Americans saw the Philippines as a valuable U.S. colony. These islands were a strategic gateway to the valuable markets of Asia. The United States wanted a share of this lucrative trade. In 1899, U.S. Secretary of State John Hay announced the "Open Door" policy. It said that the European powers would keep trading rights in China open to all nations. The Europeans went along with the policy.

In 1904–05, Japan and Russia fought a war over Manchuria. U.S. President Theodore

Roosevelt brokered a peace agreement to end the war. (He won the Nobel Peace Prize for this accomplishment.) He also arranged the "Gentlemen's Agreement" of 1907–08. San Francisco agreed to stop sending Asian students to separate schools. Japan agreed to a halt of Japanese immigration to the U.S.

## The Big Stick in the Caribbean

Both U.S. business interests and the U.S. military wanted a short, quick way to get from the Caribbean to the Pacific. Plans were made to build a canal through Panama, which was part of Colombia. The Colombian rulers refused, holding out for more money. The United States encouraged rebels to take over Panama. Then the United States stopped Colombian troops from landing and recognized the new nation. Canal building there started in 1904. The canal opened in 1914.

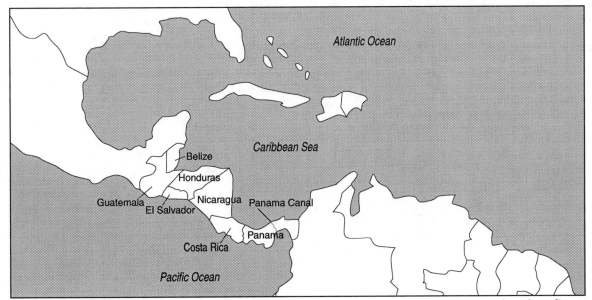

**Central America and the Panama Canal**

*(continued)*

*Focus on U.S. History:*
*The Era of Modernization Through the 1930s*

# The United States and World Affairs (continued)

President Roosevelt was fond of a West African saying: "Speak softly and carry a big stick." The "big stick" in the Caribbean was the threat—and use—of U.S. power to control Caribbean and Central American countries. The president made a formal statement of his Latin American policy in 1904. It was called the Roosevelt Corollary to the Monroe Doctrine. Under the Monroe Doctrine, no non-American nation could interfere in Latin America. Now Roosevelt claimed an "international police power" for the United States in the region. The United States, he said, would intervene in any Latin American nation that became unstable or disorderly. "Unstable" and "disorderly" conditions meant anything that was a threat to U.S. economic or military interests. Roosevelt's policy led to many cases when the United States sent troops to Central American and Caribbean nations. In other cases, the United States took over the finances of countries in this region.

## Dollar and Missionary Diplomacy

Roosevelt's successor as U.S. president was William H. Taft. He practiced what was called Dollar Diplomacy. He promoted investment of private money in Latin America. This, he reasoned, would produce stability and peace. That in turn would benefit U.S. busi-

Wilson, the foreign policy moralist, declared, "I am going to teach the South American republics to elect good men!" Latin Americans didn't think this was any of Wilson's business.

ness. U.S. troops, however, sometimes had to back up U.S. dollars.

Taft's successor was Woodrow Wilson. He was a Progressive idealist. So he added a moral tone to U.S. foreign policy. His aim was to spread democracy and the Judeo-Christian value system to nations around the world. Wilson's foreign policy was called Missionary (or Moral) Diplomacy. Wilson did practice what he preached in some areas. For example, he worked to lessen foreign meddling in China. However, he seldom followed Moral Diplomacy when U.S. interests were threatened in Latin America. In those cases, Wilson most often based his actions on the Roosevelt Corollary.

## The United States and World War I

World War I broke out in 1914. All the major nations of Europe were involved. Great Britain, France, and Russia were the Allied Powers. They fought Germany and Austria-Hungary, the Central Powers. Other nations around the world became involved as well. The United States remained neutral for most of the war. It saw itself as isolated from and having no vital interest in the problems of Europe. Most Americans agreed. Many, though, had a lot of sympathy for the Allies. (Americans of German descent tended to favor the Central Powers.)

*(continued)*

# The United States and World Affairs *(continued)*

One problem did touch the United States: the war on the seas. Great Britain blocked shipments of supplies from reaching Germany. Germany in return attacked ships that tried to reach Britain. Both civilian and military ships were targets. The German weapon was the submarine, or U-boat. President Wilson strongly protested when American lives were lost in these attacks. Germany agreed to stop attacks on civilian ships in 1916. In 1917, Germany started the attacks again. It hoped to starve Britain into surrender. Instead, it drew a strong new opponent into the war. The United States declared war on Germany.

> President Wilson felt compelled to ask Congress for a declaration of war on April 2, 1917. Ironically, his campaign slogan in 1916 had been "He kept us out of war."

The impact of the war at home was huge. Everyone was asked to help with the war effort. The economy now focused on war-related production. Women and African Americans flocked to well-paying factory jobs. Legions of blacks left the South for jobs in Northern cities. This mass movement was called the Great Migration. Propaganda posters and speeches urged people to be patriotic in many ways. This soon led to demands to ban antiwar statements. In response, the Espionage and Sedition Acts of 1917 and 1918 took away some rights of free speech. The Supreme Court upheld this.

> Anti-German feelings ran very high in the United States during the war. As a result, some common terms got new names:
> - German measles became "liberty measles."
> - Sauerkraut became "liberty cabbage."
> - Hamburger became "liberty steak."
> - Dachshunds became "liberty pups."

U.S. entry into the war was critical. The Allies were running out of money and supplies. Their troops were exhausted. Many had been fighting from lines of muddy trenches for years. U.S. supplies and fresh troops made the difference in pushing back the German spring offensive of 1918. The crumbling German army agreed to an armistice signed on November 11, 1918.

> The armistice was signed at 11 A.M. on the 11th day of the 11th month. November 11 became a national holiday called Armistice Day in 1919. That holiday is now called Veterans' Day.

*(continued)*

# The United States and World Affairs *(continued)*

## *Searching for Peace*

World War I was horribly destructive. People everywhere felt their lives were shattered. Woodrow Wilson gave a moral sense to the war with his plan for the peace process. He called it the Fourteen Points. The peace treaty ending the war should be fair to all parties, Wilson said. It should make the world "fit and safe to live in" for people of the future. It would set up an international body called the League of Nations. The League would find peaceful ways to settle all disputes between nations. War would no longer happen.

Many people shared Wilson's vision of a just and lasting peace. However, many other people did not. They wanted revenge on Germany for the war. This view shaped the peace treaties that ended the war. The treaty with Germany was called the Treaty of Versailles. It forced Germany to give up territory, and take blame for the war. It also made Germany pay huge amounts of money for wartime damage. (These payments were called **reparations**.)

President Wilson accepted the Versailles Treaty because it provided for the League of Nations. But the U.S. Senate has to approve all treaties. Several powerful Republican senators did not want the United States to be part of the League. They thought this would drag the country into European affairs and wars. Wilson went on a speaking trip across the country to build up popular support for the treaty. But he refused to compromise with the senators. The Senate rejected the treaty in March 1920.

President Wilson on the *U.S.S. George Washington* returning from Versailles.

26

*Focus on U.S. History:*
*The Era of Modernization Through the 1930s*

Name _____

Date _____

# The United States in Latin America

In the early years of the 1900s, the United States got involved in the domestic affairs of a number of Latin American countries. Where were these countries? When and why did the United States intervene? You'll create a handy reference to answer these questions by completing this activity.

**Directions:** Below is a map of the Caribbean area and Central America. On the map, locate and label the following countries. (You could shade each country a different color, too.) Also note on the map the date(s) and type of intervention for each country where the U.S. intervened.

| Cuba | Dominican Republic | Guatemala | Haiti | Honduras |
|------|--------------------|-----------|-------|----------|
| Mexico | Nicaragua | Panama | Puerto Rico | Virgin Islands |

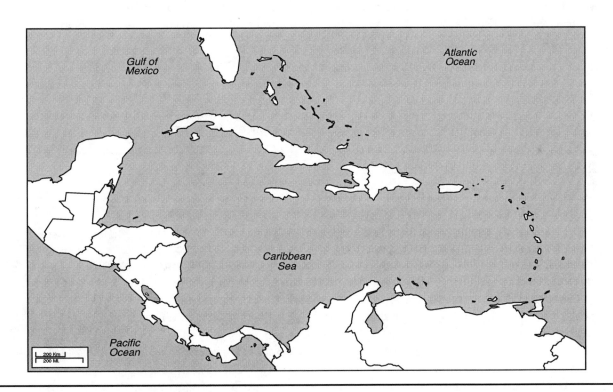

**Extra Challenge:** For each Latin American country on your map, create a brief outline that summarizes the steps of U.S. involvement in that country's domestic affairs in the first three decades of the twentieth century.

*Focus on U.S. History:*
*The Era of Modernization Through the 1930s*

# U.S. Policy and Latin America

U.S. policy toward Latin America developed and changed under different presidents, from Theodore Roosevelt to Franklin D. Roosevelt. Here are statements of Latin American policy from four different U.S. presidents and a fifth president's secretary of state.

## U.S. President Theodore Roosevelt, 1904

It is not true that the United States feels any land hunger or entertains any projects as regards the other nations of the Western Hemisphere save such as are for their own welfare. All that this country desires is to see the neighboring countries stable, orderly, and prosperous. Any country whose people conduct themselves well can count upon our hearty friendship. If a nation shows that it knows how to act with reasonable efficiency and decency in social and political matters, if it keeps order and pays its obligations, it need fear no interference from the United States. Chronic wrongdoing, or an impotence which results in a general loosening of the ties of civilized society, may in America, as elsewhere, ultimately require intervention by some civilized nation, and in the Western Hemisphere the adherence of the United States to the Monroe Doctrine may force the United States, however reluctantly, in flagrant cases of such wrongdoing or impotence, to the exercise of an international police power. . . . We would interfere with [our southern neighbors] only in the last resort, and then only if it became evident that their inability or unwillingness to do justice at home and abroad had violated the rights of the United States or had invited foreign aggression to the detriment of the entire body of American nations.

## U.S. President William Howard Taft, 1912

The diplomacy of the present administration has sought to respond to modern ideas of commercial intercourse. This policy has been characterized as substituting dollars for bullets. It is one that appeals alike to idealistic humanitarian sentiments, to the dictates of sound policy and strategy, and to legitimate commercial aims. It is an effort frankly directed to the increase of American trade upon the axiomatic principle that the government of the United States shall extend all proper support to every legitimate and beneficial American enterprise abroad. . . . [Also] the United States has been glad to encourage and support American bankers who were willing to lend a helping hand to the financial rehabilitation of [Central American] countries because this financial rehabilitation and the protection of their customhouses from being the prey of would-be dictators would remove at one stroke the menace of foreign creditors and the menace of revolutionary disorder.

*(continued)*

# U.S. Policy and Latin America *(continued)*

### U.S. President Woodrow Wilson, 1913

(OCTOBER 27, 1913) The future, ladies and gentlemen, is going to be very different for this hemisphere from the past. . . . We must prove ourselves friends [of the Latin American states] and champions upon terms of equality and honor. . . . The United States will . . . see that from no quarter are material interests made superior to human liberty and national opportunity. I say this . . . merely to fix in our consciousness what our real relationship with the rest of America is. It is the relationship of a family of mankind devoted to the development of true constitutional liberty. . . . We know that this is a cause which we are making in common with our neighbors.

(MARCH 11, 1913) Cooperation [with Latin American nations] is possible only when supported at every turn by the orderly processes of just government based upon law, not upon arbitrary or irregular force. We hold . . . that just government rests always upon the consent of the governed. . . . We shall look to make these principles the basis of mutual intercourse, respect, and helpfulness between our sister republics and ourselves.

### U.S. Secretary of State Henry L. Stimson, 1931 (Herbert Hoover, president)

The practice of this country as to the recognition of new governments has been substantially uniform from the days of the administration of Secretary of State Jefferson in 1792 to the days of Secretary of State Bryan in 1913. . . . This general policy . . . was to base the act of recognition not upon the question of the constitutional legitimacy of the new government but upon its *de facto* capacity to fulfill its obligations as a member of the family of nations. This country recognized the right of other nations to regulate their own internal affairs of government and disclaimed any attempt to base its recognition upon the correctness of their constitutional action. . . .

The present administration . . . has followed consistently the former practice of this government since the days of Jefferson. As soon as [new Latin American governments] were in control of the administrative machinery of the state, with the apparent general acquiescence of their people, and were willing and apparently able to discharge their international and conventional obligations, they were recognized by our government. And . . . we did this with as little delay as possible in order to give those sorely pressed countries the quickest possible opportunities for recovering their economic poise.

*(continued)*

# U.S. Policy and Latin America *(continued)*

**U.S. President Franklin D. Roosevelt, 1933**
  In the field of world policy I would dedicate this nation to the policy of the good neighbor—the neighbor who resolutely respects himself and, because he does so, respects the rights of others—the neighbor who respects his obligations and respects the sanctity of his agreements in and with a world of neighbors.

**Directions:** Answer the following questions about the Latin American policy statements you have just read.

1. Theodore Roosevelt's position is called the Roosevelt Corollary to the Monroe Doctrine. What was the basic U.S. policy toward Latin America under the Roosevelt Corollary?

2. Taft's policy was called Dollar Diplomacy. What was the basic U.S. policy toward Latin America under Dollar Diplomacy?

3. (a) Wilson's policy was called Missionary Diplomacy. What was the basic U.S. policy toward Latin America under Missionary Diplomacy?

   (b) How did Wilson exercise Missionary Diplomacy during the Mexican revolution?

   (c) How did Wilson act more in line with Dollar Diplomacy than Missionary Diplomacy elsewhere in Latin America?

4. Stimson was President Hoover's secretary of state. How was the Stimson/Hoover policy different from the Latin American policies that came before it?

5. Franklin D. Roosevelt's policy was called the Good Neighbor policy. What was the basic U.S. policy toward Latin America under the Good Neighbor policy?

**Extra Challenge:** Here is a 1927 statement from U.S. President Calvin Coolidge: "I am sure it is not the desire of the United States to intervene in the internal affairs of Nicaragua or of any other Central American republic. Nevertheless, it must be said that we have a very definite and special interest in the maintenance of order and good government in Nicaragua at the present time, and that the stability, prosperity, and independence of all Central American countries can never be a matter of indifference to us. The United States cannot, therefore, fail to view with deep concern any serious threat to stability and constitutional government in Nicaragua tending toward anarchy and jeopardizing American interests." Which U.S. policy toward Latin America does this statement follow?

# A Wartime Warning

During World War I, Germany used submarines to sink ships bringing supplies to Great Britain. Merchant ships were hit by torpedoes without warning. They sank quickly. Many civilians traveling on these ships died, including Americans. In 1915, the German government placed an advertisement in U.S. newspapers. Sometimes this ad appeared next to sailing notices, as shown below. On May 7, 1915, a U-boat torpedo hit the *Lusitania*. Nearly 1,200 people—women, men, and children—died, including 128 Americans.

**Directions:** Imagine you are a member of an American family in 1915. You and your family have been planning to sail to Europe on the *Lusitania*. But now you have seen this "NOTICE!" Should you change your plans? You really need to get to Europe. What should all of you do? Role-play a family discussion about this.

# Wilson's War Message

On April 2, 1917, President Wilson delivered a message to Congress asking for a declaration of war against Germany. Here is part of what he said.

### U.S. President Woodrow Wilson, 1917

The present German submarine warfare against commerce is a warfare against mankind. It is a war against all nations. American ships have been sunk, American lives taken in ways which it has stirred us very deeply to learn of; but the ships and people of other neutral and friendly nations have been sunk and overwhelmed in the waters in the same way.

. . . We will not choose the path of submission and suffer the most sacred rights of our nation and our people to be ignored or violated. The wrongs against which we now array ourselves are no common wrongs; they cut to the very roots of human life.

Our object . . . is to vindicate the principles of peace and justice in the life of the world as against selfish and autocratic power. . . . Neutrality is no longer feasible or desirable where the peace of the world is involved and the freedom of its peoples. . . .

The world must be made safe for democracy. Its peace must be planted upon the tested foundations of political liberty. We have no selfish ends to serve. We desire no conquest, no dominion. We seek no indemnities for ourselves, no material compensation for the sacrifices we shall freely make. We are but one of the champions of the rights of mankind. We shall be satisfied when those rights have been made as secure as the faith and the freedom of nations can make them.

. . . It is a fearful thing to lead this great peaceful people into war, into the most terrible and disastrous of all wars, civilization itself seeming to be in the balance. But the right is more precious than peace, and we shall fight for the things which we have always carried nearest our hearts—for democracy, for the right of those who submit to authority to have a voice in their own governments, for the rights and liberties of small nations, for a universal dominion of right by such a concert of free peoples as shall bring peace and safety to all nations and make the world itself at last free.

**Directions:** Now read Senator Norris's opposing reply to Wilson's war message. Then you will use the "Enter the War: Yes or No?" activity sheet to evaluate Wilson's and Norris's statements.

# Don't Enter the War!

Six U.S. senators voted against declaring war on Germany and entering World War I. Senator George Norris of Nebraska was one of them. He gave his reasons against entering the war in a U.S. Senate speech. Here is part of what Norris said.

---

**U.S. Senator George W. Norris, 1917**

The reason given by the President in asking Congress to declare war against Germany is that the German Government has declared certain war zones, within which, by the use of submarines, she sinks, without notice, American ships and destroys American lives. . . . The first war zone was declared by Great Britain. . . . The first German war zone was declared . . . three months after the British war zone was declared. . . . Thus we have the two declarations of the two Governments, each declaring a military zone and warning neutral shipping from going into the prohibited area. England sought to make her order effective by the use of submerged mines. Germany sought to make her order effective by the use of submarines. Both of these orders were illegal and contrary to all international law as well as the principles of humanity. . . .

The only difference is that in the case of Germany we have persisted in our protest, while in the case of England we have submitted. What was our duty as a Government and what were our rights when we were confronted with these extraordinary orders declaring these military zones? First, we could have defied both of them and could have gone to war against both of these nations. . . . Second, we had the technical right to defy one and to acquiesce in the other. Third, we could, while denouncing them both as illegal, have acquiesced in them both and thus remained neutral with both sides. . . . Fourth, we might have declared an embargo against the shipping from American ports of any merchandise to either one of these Governments that persisted in maintaining its military zone. In my judgment, if we had pursued this course, the zones would have been of short duration. . . .

There are a great many American citizens who feel that we owe it as a duty to humanity to take part in this war. Many instances of cruelty and inhumanity can be found on both sides.

. . . The enormous profits of munition manufacturers, stockbrokers, and bond dealers must be still further increased by our entrance into the war. . . . Their object in having war and in preparing for war is to make money. Human suffering and the sacrifice of human life are necessary, but Wall Street considers only the dollars and the cents.

---

# Enter the War: Yes or No?

**Directions:** Evaluate President Wilson's arguments for entering World War I and Senator Norris's arguments for not entering the war by answering the questions below and completing the final exercise.

1. What two main reasons does Wilson give for entering the war? _____

   _____

   _____

2. Why is German unrestricted submarine warfare *not* a reason for the United States to go to war, according to Norris?

   _____

   _____

3. What other reasons does Norris give for not entering the war? _____

   _____

   _____

4. What policy should the United States have taken about the threats to its shipping, according to Norris?

   _____

   _____

5. Now evaluate the Norris arguments compared with Wilson's position in his war message. Discuss, debate, or write an opinion paper. Are Norris's points about the dual war zones valid? Could the change of policy Norris suggested eliminate the problem of ships being sunk? Was the United States really making the world safe for democracy by entering the war?

   _____

   _____

   _____

   _____

   _____

   _____

34 *Focus on U.S. History:
The Era of Modernization Through the 1930s*

# Weapons of the War

**Directions:** World War I featured many new weapons that were far more destructive than weapons used in earlier wars. Identify how these new weapons made World War I so much more destructive.

◆ **Tank**

Effect: _____

_____

_____

_____

◆ **Machine Gun**

Effect: _____

_____

_____

_____

◆ **German U-boat**

Effect: _____

_____

_____

_____

◆ **War Plane**

Effect: _____

_____

_____

_____

German U-boat

◆ **Gas Mask**

What weapon does this item defend against?

_____

Effect of weapon: _____

_____

_____

*Focus on U.S. History:*
*The Era of Modernization Through the 1930s*

# Life in the Trenches

Life in the trenches of World War I was a miserable experience for the infantry soldiers who manned the deep, often muddy ditches. Here is one soldier's account of his first experience, arriving at the trenches. It is from his World War I memoir *Over the Top*, published in 1917. (A dugout was an underground chamber dug out of the side of a trench.)

### Guy Empey, World War I soldier, 1917

Next evening, we took over our sector of the line. In single file we wended our way through a zigzag communication trench, six inches deep with mud. . . . The boy in front of me named Prentice crumpled up without a word. A piece of shell had gone through his shrapnel-proof helmet. I felt sick and weak.

In about thirty minutes we reached the front line. It was dark as pitch. Every now and then a German star shell would pierce the blackness out in front with its silvery light. I was trembling all over, and felt very lonely and afraid. . . .

I sat on the fire step of the trench with the rest of the men. . . . Pretty soon it started to rain. We put on our "macks" (raincoats), but they were not much protection. The rain trickled down our backs, and it was not long before we were wet and cold. . . .

I must have slept for two or three hours, . . . the sleep that comes from cold, wet, and sheer exhaustion. Suddenly, the earth seemed to shake and a thunderclap burst in my ears. I opened my eyes,—I was splashed all over with sticky mud, and men were picking themselves up from the bottom of the trench. . . . The man on my left lay still. I rubbed the mud from my face, and an awful sight met my gaze—his head was smashed to a pulp. . . . A German "Minnie" (trench mortar) had exploded in the next traverse. . . .

That dugout was muddy. The men slept in mud, washed in mud, ate mud, and dreamed mud. I had never before realized that so much discomfort and misery could be contained in those three little letters, M U D. The floor of the dugout was an inch deep in water. Outside it was raining cats and dogs and thin rivulets were trickling down the steps. From the airshaft above me came a drip, drip, drip. . . . The air was foul. . . . It was cold.

**World War I soldiers in trench**

**Directions:** Imagine you are a World War I soldier fighting from the trenches. Write a series of diary entries or letters home describing your experiences. Tell about specific incidents, discomforts, and dangers. Add some humor to what you write. Share these accounts with classmates.

# War Propaganda

Propaganda posters were an important part of World War I. All the major nations used them to promote various war aims. Study the posters shown on this page and the next. Then answer these questions about each one: What war aim does this poster promote? What emotional appeal, symbol, or slogan does the poster use to get its message across?

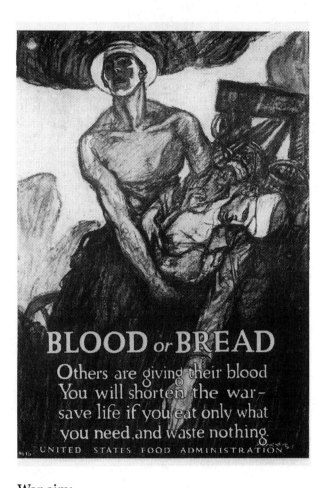

War aim: _____

Appeal, symbol, slogan: _____

_____

_____

_____

War aim: _____

Appeal, symbol, slogan: _____

_____

_____

_____

*(continued)*

## War Propaganda *(continued)*

War aim:_____

Appeal, symbol, slogan: _____

_____

_____

_____

_____

War aim: _____

Appeal, symbol, slogan: _____

_____

_____

_____

*Focus on U.S. History:*
*The Era of Modernization Through the 1930s*

# Women and the War

During World War I, many U.S. women took over jobs men left to become soldiers. Some women took factory jobs in wartime industries—for example, making bullets, or welding warplanes and armaments. Others worked to keep public utilities in service, drove delivery trucks, and kept other industries running.

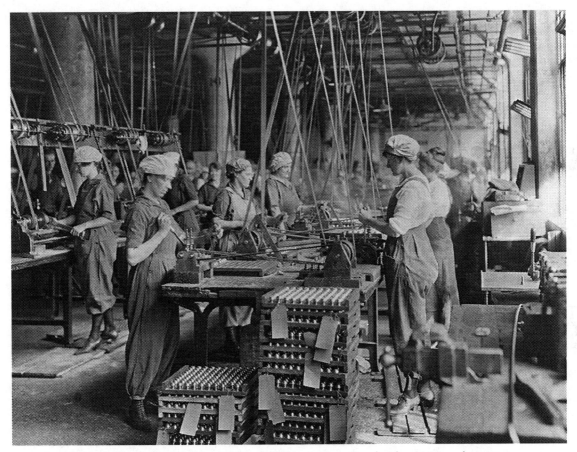

Female workers slot fuses at Gray & Davis Co., Cambridge, Massachusetts.

**Directions:** Working at wartime jobs brought many women out of the home and into the labor force for the first time. Imagine you are a young woman working an eight-hour day and earning your own living for the first time. Keep a diary about your experiences. What new things do you learn to do? How is your life different? How do you feel about your life and your fellow workers? What do you do when the war ends and a returned male soldier takes over your job? To get background for your diary, find more pictures of wartime women at work, and read some contemporary accounts of women war workers.

# Your Right to Free Speech

Wartime hysteria about disloyalty, aliens, spies, and so on, was at fever pitch in the United States during World War I. This led to the passage of the Espionage and Sedition Acts of 1917 and 1918. Here's part of what the act of 1918 said about limits on free speech during the war.

> . . . Whoever, when the United States is at war, shall wilfully . . . obstruct the recruiting or enlistment service of the United States, [or] utter, print, write, or publish any disloyal, profane, scurrilous, or abusive language about the form of government of the United States, or the constitution of the United States, or the military or naval forces of the United States, or the flag, . . . or any language intended to bring the form of government . . . or the military or naval forces . . . or the flag . . . of the United States into contempt, scorn, . . . or disrepute, . . . or shall wilfully . . . urge, incite, or advocate any curtailment of production in this country of any thing or things necessary or essential to the prosecution of the war . . . shall be punished by a fine of not more than $10,000 or imprisonment for not more than 20 years, or both.

**Directions:** Which, if any, of these things would have gotten you arrested under the Espionage and Sedition Acts of 1917 and 1918? Check each that would have.

_____ 1. You publicly criticize President Wilson's foreign policy toward Mexico.

_____ 2. You question whether the national draft law is a violation of the U.S. Constitution.

_____ 3. You publish an article urging workers of the world to unite in an effort to end the war.

_____ 4. You complain that wartime taxes are too high.

_____ 5. You write pamphlets opposing U.S. soldiers being sent to take part in the Russian civil war.

_____ 6. You make an antiwar speech.

_____ 7. You criticize the American Red Cross and its wartime activities.

_____ 8. You mail leaflets urging noncompliance to men who have gotten notices to report to the U.S. Army to be drafted into military service.

_____ 9. You criticize the wartime activities of the YMCA.

# The League of Nations: Yes or No?

The Treaty of Versailles ended the war with Germany. This treaty contained a plan to set up a League of Nations, an association of the world's nations. The question of whether or not the United States should join such a league was a big part of the debate about accepting or rejecting the Treaty of Versailles. Here are two views. Senator Borah was one of the country's leading isolationists and League opponents. President Wilson saw the League as the most important achievement of the wartime victory.

---

### U.S. President Woodrow Wilson, 1919

The heart of the Covenant [setting up the League] is that there shall be no war. . . . All the members of the League . . . agree that they will never go to war without first having done one or other of two things—either submitted the question at issue to arbitration, . . . or . . . submitted it to discussion by the council of the League [and] cool off for nine months before they [go to war]. . . . Every member of the League promises to respect and preserve as against external aggression . . . the territorial integrity and existing political independence of every other member of the League.

---

### U.S. Senator William Borah, 1919

We are a part of the European turmoils and conflicts from the time we enter this League. . . . Is there any limitation of the jurisdiction of the [League's] Council or of the Assembly upon the question of peace or war? . . . How shall you keep from meddling in the affairs of Europe or keep Europe from meddling in the affairs of America? . . . Mr. President, there is another and even a more commanding reason why I shall record my vote against this treaty. . . . It is in conflict with the right of our people to govern themselves, free from all restraint, legal or moral, of foreign powers. . . . Is there any guarantee of peace other than the guarantee which comes of the control of the war-making power by the people?

---

**Directions:** Read some more opinions for and against the United States joining the League of Nations. Then role-play a debate between people on the two sides. Take the roles of real and/or imaginary people of the times (1919–1920). In addition to Borah, one of the strongest opponents of the League was Senator Henry Cabot Lodge of Massachusetts.

# The Roaring Twenties

The objective of this unit is to help students understand the changes that occurred in the United States from the end of World War I to the eve of the Great Depression. Americans in the twenties turned their backs on war and enjoyed economic boom times. The automobile began changing the face of America, and mass advertising created a great demand for new consumer products. Young people shed Victorian attitudes, and a freer "New Woman" developed. Mass media—especially movies and radio shows—helped create a mass culture. Sports super-stars emerged. Social tensions also grew. As African Americans continued their migration in huge numbers from the rural South to jobs in the urban North, racial conflicts increased, and ghettoes formed in northern cities. Intolerance of radicals, minorities, and immigrants caused a red scare and Palmer raids, strict immigration quotas, and the rebirth of the Ku Klux Klan. This unit's activities are designed to draw students into a better understanding of these changes in U.S. life during the 1920s.

# Student Activities

**The Urban-Rural Change** presents a graph showing the growth of urban and rural populations in the United States from 1840 to 1940. **Reading the Urban-Rural Graph** helps students interpret the graph by answering a series of questions. The Extra Challenge asks students to create a series of pie charts showing the percentages of the U.S. population that were urban and rural in ten-year increments from 1900 to 1940.

**The Great Migration** shows in a chart how much the African-American population increased or decreased in selected southern and northern states in the three decades from 1900 to 1930—the population shift known as the Great Migration. Students create a bar graph that shows these population changes. The Extra Challenge asks students to write a very persuasive article or editorial, like those that appeared in the *Chicago Defender*, urging southern blacks to migrate to the North.

**Returning African-American Soldiers** presents a strong appeal, written by W. E. B. DuBois, to black soldiers returning from World War I to reject racist treatment. Students either identify specific examples of the wrongs against African Americans that DuBois lists or put themselves in the place of a returning black soldier and describe the reception they get and their reaction to it.

**African-American Life in the North** presents an excerpt from the short story "The Typewriter," by Harlem Renaissance writer Dorothy West, describing a black man's disillusion with the life in the North he had migrated from the South to establish. Students imagine themselves as a young, rural southern black who has moved to a large northern city and describe their experiences and feelings about the move.

**Immigration Ups and Downs** presents students with a graph of immigration to the United States from 1913 to 1935. **Reading the Immigration Graph** helps students interpret the graph by answering a series of questions. The Extra Challenge asks students to construct a graph showing immigration as a percentage of total U.S. population during the years from 1910 to 1940. (Students have been asked to construct similar graphs for other time periods in earlier books in this series. Population figures are available in *Historical Statistics of the United States*.)

**The "New Woman"** shows pictures of women enjoying less restrictive aspects of their lives in the 1920s. Students identify how each thing pictured expanded women's rights and freedoms in the twenties. The Extra Challenge asks students to create and role-play a dialogue between a flapper and her parents about the girl's appearance and activities.

**Women and Work, 1920s Style**, presents a description of "modern" young working women from a 1926 magazine article. Students compare this view of women and work with the view they read in the Unit 1 activity, "Women and Work."

**The Great American Game** is a vivid description of the excitement of watching a well-played baseball game, drawing students into the 1920s passion for sports. Students create a photo essay of the development of professional baseball in the early twentieth century or write their own description of a sport they enjoy participating in or watching, using this excerpt as a writing model.

**Twenties Talk** introduces students to some of the trendy new words and phrases that the Jazz Age added to the American language. Once students identify what each listed word and phrase means, they can try to carry on a twenties conversation as sheiks and shebas. The Extra Challenge asks students to give any current slang terms for the listed twenties terms and identify any of the twenties terms that are still used today.

**Sports Stars** highlights the twenties passion for sports by listing the sports superstars who emerged during the decade. Students match each star with her or his sport. The Extra Challenge asks students to research and report on the sports career of one of the listed stars.

**The Automobile and the American Landscape** draws students into a consideration of how the automobile changed the American scene. Students identify photographs of some things, like gas stations and roadside quick-food stands, that are familiar to us today but were unknown before car ownership became widespread. Then they explain why each of these things developed because of the automobile.

# The Roaring Twenties

## The Booming Economy

In 1920, Americans turned their backs on war. They were happy to enjoy peace and good times. They didn't much care about Progressive reform anymore. They liked the call of their new president, Warren Harding, for a "return to normalcy."

The twenties, though, weren't a return to old times. They were a leap into an economic boom. Workers' wages were up, and unemployment was down. Demand for consumer goods was high, and factories responded with more goods. Business owners learned new, more efficient ways to produce things. Perhaps most efficient was the moving assembly line. Henry Ford had developed it for his automobile plant before World War I. Now it spread to most industries.

Washing machine

Consumer purchasing drove this economic boom. Advertising pumped up consumer spending. People who couldn't afford to pay cash bought on credit. Homes filled with radios, washing machines, refrigerators. Many people now owned cars. This began to change the face of America. The highway system grew. Roadside businesses multiplied. Tourism increased. Suburbs appeared and spread.

## Mass Culture in the Twenties

U.S. culture and society changed in many ways during the 1920s. For the first time in U.S. history, more people now lived in urban than rural areas. Young people scorned old traditions. They discarded the strict Victorian ways of their parents. Young couples went off alone on dates. They got together with other couples for "necking" and "petting" parties. Many older people were shocked.

> "New Woman" Margaret Sanger worked hard to spread information about birth control.

Particularly shocking was the "flapper." She cut her hair short. She wore ever-shorter skirts and little underwear. She used makeup freely. She stayed out dancing till all hours, drank alcohol, and smoked cigarettes. The flapper was one type of the "New Woman" of the 1920s. Women wanted more social and economic freedom. More and more women worked outside the home now. They had gotten used to that during the war. More careers opened to women. Divorce laws were more fair to women.

> Alice Paul and her National Woman's party pressed for passage of an Equal Rights Amendment to the U.S. Constitution.

*(continued)*

*Focus on U.S. History:
The Era of Modernization Through the 1930s*

# The Roaring Twenties *(continued)*

Mass media became very popular during the 1920s. Viewers flocked to modern movie "palaces" and small-town movie theaters. They were drawn by favorite screen stars. Fans loved comedian Charlie Chaplin, vamp Theda Bara, and heartthrob Rudolph Valentino. At home, families gathered around their radio. A favorite show was "Amos 'n' Andy." This comedy centered around two black men played by two white actors.

Sports also became very popular during the twenties. Americans had more free time to engage in and watch sports. They also could listen to play-by-play accounts on radio. A series of sports superstars emerged. Babe Ruth was foremost among them. Social dances became more athletic and vigorous too, like the Charleston.

## African Americans and the Harlem Renaissance

African Americans suffered dashed hopes after World War I. The move of many southern blacks to northern cities continued during the 1920s. Housing shortages in "black" areas of the cities—ghettoes—became severe. Rents soared. Unemployment rose, as wartime jobs vanished. Whites became more and more hostile. The Ku Klux Klan revived in 1915. It directed its violence toward blacks in both the South and the North. Race riots broke out during the summer of 1919. A number of African American soldiers who returned home from the war were lynched. Some were still in uniform.

In response to these troubles, African Americans became more assertive. Marcus

Garvey was a native of Jamaica. He promoted black pride with his Back to Africa movement. "Up you mighty race, you can accomplish what you will!" he called. The 1920s also saw a creative outpouring of African-American literature, painting, and music. It was centered in the nation's largest black community, Harlem, in New York City. So it became known as the Harlem Renaissance. The artists of this renaissance drew on black culture, present and past, and their own feelings of racial pride and anger to create powerful works.

**Marcus Garvey**

*(continued)*

# The Roaring Twenties (continued)

## Resistance to Change

As always in times of change, some people didn't like what was happening. When World War I ended, people seemed still ready to fight. The Ku Klux Klan spread rapidly. Its enemies, in addition to blacks, were foreigners, Catholics, and Jews. Many workers went on strike for higher wages. Nonstrikers thought radicals were stirring up labor unrest. They linked radicals with communists. Soon a "red scare" swept the country. A series of "Palmer raids" arrested 6,000 people, mostly immigrants. (The raids were named for U.S. Attorney General Mitchell Palmer.) Many of the people arrested were U.S. citizens. Few were radicals.

The anti-immigrant feelings continued into the 1920s. Immigration had nearly stopped during World War I. When the war ended, people from abroad flooded into the United States. Most were Catholics and Jews from southern and eastern Europe. Many people also came from Mexico. This alarmed white nativists. In response, Congress passed new laws in 1921 and 1924. These laws placed quotas on immigration from each country. The number of people entering the United States from southern and eastern Europe dropped abruptly.

Many people still lived in the rural sections of the country. They didn't like the new urban culture. The Eighteenth Amendment to the Constitution prohibited making or selling alcohol. This was known as Prohibition. Rural people mostly were in favor of Prohibition. Many urban dwellers ignored the no-alcohol laws. Many country people also returned to basic religious beliefs, called **fundamentalism**. These people were strongly opposed to Darwin's concept of evolution. They said such ideas denied the divine origin of life. This clash led to the famous Scopes trial. A schoolteacher was charged with breaking Tennessee law by teaching evolution. The trial raised important questions about the place of religion in public school. These questions would be revisited later in U.S. history.

The Scopes evolution trial caught the public imagination. The defense attorney, Clarence Darrow, was famous. So was the prosecutor, William Jennings Bryan. He had run for U.S. president three times. Darrow grilled Bryan about his beliefs in the literal truth of the Bible. A fascinated audience listened to the first trial ever broadcast (on radio).

*Focus on U.S. History:*
*The Era of Modernization Through the 1930s*

# The Urban-Rural Change

The graph below shows the growth of urban and rural populations in the United States. (Urban areas are heavily populated; *urban* refers to cities. Rural areas are lightly rather than densely populated; *rural* refers to the country, or countryside.) Use the graph to answer the questions on the next page.

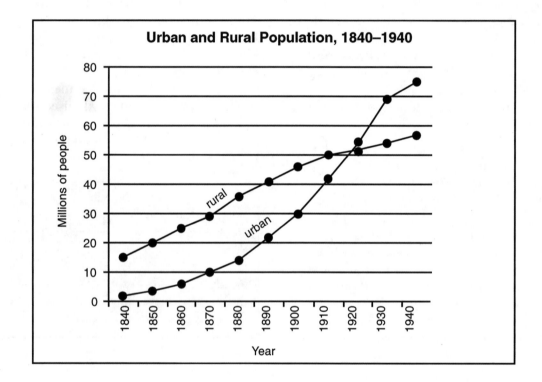

**Urban and Rural Population, 1840–1940**

*Millions of people* (y-axis: 0, 10, 20, 30, 40, 50, 60, 70, 80)

*Year* (x-axis: 1840, 1850, 1860, 1870, 1880, 1890, 1900, 1910, 1920, 1930, 1940)

rural

urban

*(continued)*

*Focus on U.S. History:*
*The Era of Modernization Through the 1930s*

Name _____

Date _____

# The Urban-Rural Change *(continued)*

**Directions:** Answer the following questions about the Urban and Rural Population graph.

1. What shift in U.S. population had occurred by 1920? _____

   _____

   Did this pattern continue throughout the 1920s and 1930s? _____

2. About how many people lived in rural areas of the United States in 1900? _____

   in urban areas? _____

3. About how many people lived in rural areas of the United States in 1930? _____

   in urban areas? _____

4. How would you describe the rate of growth in the urban population as compared with the rural population in the years after 1900?

   _____

   _____

   Why were these changes taking place? _____

   _____

   _____

   _____

   _____

---

**Extra Challenge:** Calculate the percentages of the U.S. population that were urban and rural in the years 1900, 1910, 1920, 1930, and 1940. Show these percentages on a series of pie charts.

---

49

*Focus on U.S. History:*
*The Era of Modernization Through the 1930s*

Name _____

Date _____

# The Great Migration

**Directions:** The chart below tells how much the population of African Americans increased or decreased in selected southern and northern states in the three decades from 1900 to 1930. This population shift is known as the Great Migration. Create a bar graph that shows these population changes.

| Northern States | 1900–1910 | 1910–1920 | 1920–1930 |
|---|---|---|---|
| Illinois | +23,500 | +69,800 | +119,300 |
| Michigan | + 1,900 | +38,700 | + 86,100 |
| Missouri | + 1,000 | +27,200 | + 35,900 |
| New York | +35,800 | +63,100 | +172,800 |
| Pennsylvania | +32,900 | +82,500 | +101,700 |
| **Southern States** | **1900–1910** | **1910–1920** | **1920–1930** |
| Alabama | –22,100 | – 70,800 | – 80,700 |
| Georgia | –16,200 | – 74,700 | –260,000 |
| Mississippi | –30,900 | –129,600 | – 68,800 |
| South Carolina | –72,000 | – 74,500 | –204,300 |
| Virginia | –49,300 | – 27,200 | –117,200 |

**Extra Challenge:** The *Chicago Defender* was an African-American newspaper. It published articles and editorials urging blacks to "leave the benighted land" of the South and come to the North. Imagine you are an editor of the *Defender*. Write one of those very persuasive articles or editorials.

*Focus on U.S. History:*
*The Era of Modernization Through the 1930s*

# Returning African-American Soldiers

W. E. B. DuBois was an outstanding African-American writer, scholar, and leader. When black soldiers returned from service in World War I, DuBois made a strong call for them to reject racism in America and demand equal treatment. Here is an excerpt from that call. It appeared in *The Crisis*, the publication of the National Association for the Advancement of Colored People, in 1919.

We are returning from war! . . . For bleeding France and what she means and has meant and will mean to us and humanity and against the threat of German race arrogance, we fought gladly and to the last drop of blood; for America and her highest ideals, we fought in far-off hope; for the dominant southern oligarchy entrenched in Washington, we fought in bitter resignation. For the America that represents and gloats in lynching, disfranchisement, caste, brutality and devilish insult—for this, in the hateful upturning and mixing of things, we were forced by vindictive fate to fight, also.

But today we return! . . . We stand again to look America squarely in the face. . . . We sing: This country of ours, despite all its better souls have done and dreamed, is yet a shameful land.

It *lynches*. . . . It *disfranchises* its own citizens. . . . It encourages *ignorance*. . . . It *steals* from us. . . . It *insults* us.

This is the country to which we Soldiers of Democracy return. This is the fatherland for which we fought! But it is *our* fatherland. It was right for us to fight. The faults of *our* country are *our* faults. Under similar circumstances, we would fight again. But by the God of Heaven, we are cowards and jackasses if now that that war is over, we do not marshal every ounce of our brain and brawn to fight a sterner, longer, more unbending battle against the forces of hell in our own land.

We *return*. We *return from fighting*. We *return fighting*.

Make way for Democracy! We saved it in France, and by the Great Jehovah, we will save it in the United States of America, or know the reason why.

**Directions:** Complete either of the following activities.

1. Identify and define specific examples of wrongs against African Americans in the World War I era that DuBois lists (i.e., lynching, disfranchisement, and stealing).

2. Imagine you are an African-American soldier returning to the U.S. from service in World War I. What kind of reception do you get? Write an account of your treatment.

# African-American Life in the North

Between 1915 and 1930, nearly one million blacks left their homes and homeland in the South to move to the North. Life in this northern "promised land" was not always what black migrants had hoped. Here is an excerpt from the short story "The Typewriter" about one such migrant. The story's author is Dorothy West, a teenage writer of the Harlem Renaissance.

> It occurred to him, as he eased past the bulging knees of an Irish wash lady and forced an apologetic passage down the aisle of the crowded [trolley] car, that more than anything in all the world he wanted not to go home. . . . He knew quite suddenly that he hated his flat [apartment] and his family and his friends. . . .
>
> He shuffled down the street, an abject little man of fifty-odd years, in an ageless overcoat that flapped in the wind. He was cold, and he hated the north, and particularly Boston, and saw suddenly a barefoot pickaninny sitting on a fence in the hot, Southern sun with a piece of steaming corn bread and a piece of fried salt pork in either grimy hand.
>
> He was tired, and he wanted his supper, but he didn't want the beans, and frankfurters, and light bread that Net would undoubtedly have. . . .
>
> He thought of that eager Negro lad of seventeen who had come North to seek his fortune. He had walked jauntily down Boylston Street, and even his own kind had laughed at the incongruity of him. But he had thrown up his head and promised himself: "You'll have an office here some day. With plate-glass windows and a real mahogany desk." But, though he didn't know it then, he was not the progressive type. And he became successively, in the years, bell boy, porter, waiter, cook, and finally janitor in a down town office building.

**Directions:** Imagine you are a young, rural southern black who has moved to a large northern city. Write a series of diary entries describing your experiences and feelings. How is your life different? Are you better off financially? Are your living conditions better, or worse? In what ways? How have your social life and family life changed? Is life on the whole really better for African Americans in the North than in the South?

# Immigration Ups and Downs

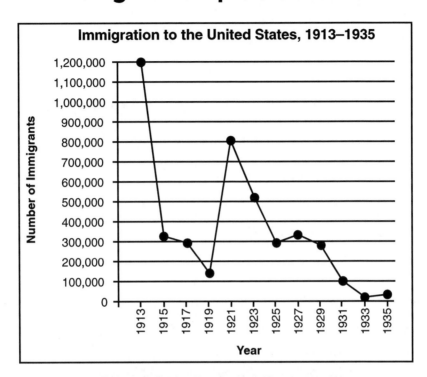

## Immigration to the United States, 1913–1935

53

*Focus on U.S. History:*
*The Era of Modernization Through the 1930s*

# Reading the Immigration Graph

**Directions:** Use the information on the immigration graph to answer these questions.

1. In which year was immigration to the United States greatest? _____

   Approximately how many immigrants came to the U.S. in that year? _____

2. During what years did immigration drop after the high? _____

   Why did immigration drop during those years? _____

   _____

3. In which year was immigration second highest? _____

   Approximately how many immigrants came to the U.S. in that year? _____

4. What happened to immigration during the 1920s? _____

   _____

   Why did immigration drop during those years? _____

   _____

5. What happened to immigration during the 1930s? _____

   _____

   Why did immigration drop during those years? _____

   _____

6. Approximately how many fewer immigrants came to the United States in 1933 than arrived in 1913?

   _____

> **Extra Challenge:** Construct a graph showing immigration as a percentage of the total U.S. population during the years from 1910 to 1940.

# The "New Woman"

Life for many U.S. women in the 1920s was notably less restrictive than in earlier years. The newly liberated female was called the "New Woman."

**Directions:** Explain how each item below expanded women's rights and freedom in the 1920s.

◆ **The right to vote**

Liberating effect: _____

_____

_____

_____

◆ **Washing machine**

Liberating Effect: _____

_____

_____

_____

◆ **1920s flapper**

Liberating effect: _____

_____

_____

_____

**Extra Challenge:** Create and role-play a dialogue between a flapper and her parents discussing the girl's choice of clothing, bobbed hairstyle, boyfriend, late hours, dating, cigarettes, makeup, and so on.

# Women and Work, 1920s Style

Ideas about women, work, and independence became a lot more modern in the 1920s than they had been earlier. The following paragraphs describe the typical young working woman of the twenties, whom this writer calls "the flapper." The excerpt is from an article written by journalist Samuel Crowther, published in *Collier's* magazine in 1926.

The real flapper is what used to be known as the "poor working girl"—who, if the accounts are true, dragged herself off day by day to work until someone came along and married her. . . . In dress she is as standardized as a chain hotel. . . . The outstanding characteristic of the flapper is not her uniform but her independence and her will to be prosperous.

She is no clinging vine. I was in the office of the president of a good-sized bank on the Pacific Coast when his daughter and several of her high-school friends burst in—flappers all. We got to talking and I found that these girls, not one of whom had any need to work, all intended to find jobs during the summer, and they thought that most of the girls in school would do the same. They all wanted to know how to make a living—and to have a good time doing it. That seems to be common everywhere.

Girls will no longer marry men who can merely support them—they can support themselves better than can many of the men of their own age. They have awakened to the fact that the "superior sex" stuff is all bunk. . . .

The flapper wants to look well, and she is willing to provide for herself—employers everywhere told me that the women were doing better work than the men, and they do seem to be mentally more alert.

**Directions:** Compare this view of women and work with the one you read in the Unit 1 activity, "Women and Work." How have 1920s women's and men's attitudes toward work changed since the beginning of the twentieth century? What accounts for this change? How does this description of 1920s working young women differ from today's working young women?

# The Great American Game

Sports became extremely popular in the 1920s, especially baseball, "the great American game." Why were sports in general and baseball in particular so popular? Here's a description that expresses the thrill of the game for its excited spectators. The author, J. P. Casey, was both a professional baseball player and a dentist. The essay this excerpt is from was first published in *The Independent* in 1906, but it reflects well the twenties sports enthusiasm.

And what a game it is to watch! There's work for two or three pairs of the sharpest eyes to see all that is going on. There's the man that is trying to steal from first base to second, lying far out from first base, with a spring in his body like a hickory bow, ready to dart for second base and hurtle thru dust to immortal glory if he sees the smallest sign of weakening in catcher or pitcher. He is brave, but not rash; he is far out, but not too far; for the pitcher is watching him with half an eye and stands ready to launch a Jovian thunderbolt that will dash him to pieces if he is off base.

Lou Gehrig, the "Iron Horse"
of 1920s and 1930s baseball

Tense thousands watch. The fate of empires hangs on Kelly's slide.

But this is only one little detail. At the same time there is to be seen the great battle between pitcher and batter and also the runner trying to steal home from third base. A good game is a three-ringed circus with a tingle of excitement for every moment. When a base hit is made, with two men on bases in a close game, lightning looks slow and poky in comparison with the way things happen out on the diamond; the ball sizzles about, burning the air, the men on the field dart like streaks, while on the stands twenty thousand madmen worship their gods with a great outcry.

Such is baseball, our baseball! A game that clutches spectators and squeezes them till they yell; a game that makes centenarians dance and howl and throw peanut shells at the umpire. There's nothing like it in the way of games.

**Directions:** Complete either or both of the following activities.

1. Create a photo essay of the development of professional baseball in the late nineteenth and early twentieth centuries.

2. Write your own description of a sport you enjoy participating in or watching. Use an enthusiastic and lively style like Casey's.

Name ______________________________

Date ______________________________

**UNIT 3**
**WORKSHEET 10**

# Twenties Talk

**Directions:** Can you talk like a twenties flapper or sheik? What's a flapper? or a sheik? Tell what each of these 1920s words and phrases means or refers to.

flapper ______________________________

jellybean ______________________________

It ______________________________

sheik ______________________________

sheba ______________________________

snugglepup ______________________________

flat tire ______________________________

two-timer ______________________________

big cheese ______________________________

goof ______________________________

lounge lizard ______________________________

the cat's meow ______________________________

double date ______________________________

cheaters ______________________________

giggle water ______________________________

ossified ______________________________

gams ______________________________

whoopee ______________________________

park ______________________________

copacetic ______________________________

banana oil ______________________________

horsefeathers ______________________________

carry a torch ______________________________

bee's knees ______________________________

jake ______________________________

spiffy ______________________________

neck ______________________________

dogs ______________________________

**Extra Challenge:** Give any current slang terms for 1920s terms listed above. Check off any of the 1920s terms that are still used today.

# Sports Stars

**Directions:** Sports became extremely popular in the years after World War I. Sports lovers of those times avidly followed the careers of some great stars. Listed below are the names of these sports stars, along with the sports they starred in. Can you match each name with the correct sport? Write the letter of the sport next to the name it goes with.

_____ Babe Ruth         (a) baseball

_____ Red Grange        (b) boxing

_____ Bill Tilden         (c) football

_____ Man o' War        (d) golf

_____ Gertrude Ederle     (e) horse racing

_____ Knute Rockne      (f) swimming

_____ Jim Thorpe         (g) tennis

_____ Helen Wills         (h) track and field

_____ Bobby Jones

_____ Johnny Weissmuller

_____ Jack Dempsey

**Babe Ruth**

> **Extra Challenge:** Research and report on the sports career of one of the stars listed above. Add photos to your report. What accomplishments made this star so outstanding in his or her sport?

*Focus on U.S. History:
The Era of Modernization Through the 1930s*

# The Automobile and the American Landscape

In 1908, Henry Ford brought the Model T to the American public. Millions of Americans could now afford to own a car. By the 1920s, car ownership had become common. As a result, the look of America changed. Listed below are some things familiar to us today that were unknown before the car spread across the United States. Explain why each of these things developed.

◆ **Billboards**

Why developed: _____

_____

_____

◆ **Roadside quick-food restaurants**

Why developed: _____

_____

_____

◆ **Gas stations**

Why developed: _____

_____

_____

◆ **Tourist courts**

Why developed: _____

_____

_____

◆ **Suburbs**

Why developed: _____

_____

_____

# The Great Depression

The objective of this unit is to guide students to an understanding of the causes of the Great Depression and the ways in which it affected American society. While the U.S. economy had boomed during the 1920s, serious economic flaws existed. Some important industries were in decline, farmers were in deep trouble, and consumer goods were in severe overproduction. The stock market crash of 1929 revealed just how serious the economic flaws were. Banks and businesses failed, people lost their jobs and their homes and their life savings, and farms in the Midwest turned into dust bowls. The economy refused to recover with President Hoover's cautious policies, and millions upon millions of Americans seemed to have become permanently unemployed. Even during these dark days, however, people found release in movies and books and parlor games. This unit's activities are designed to draw students into a better understanding of the Great Depression.

# Student Activities

**Your Economic Problems** has students imagine themselves to be specific Americans and tell how the problems with the economy of the 1920s (problems that together helped bring on the Great Depression) are affecting their lives.

**Presidential Elections: 1928 and 1932** shows results of the 1928 and 1932 presidential elections on state-by-state maps. A series of questions guides students through an analysis of the election results and the changes that occurred from 1928 to 1932. The Extra Challenge asks students to relate other twentieth-century presidential election results to those in 1928 and 1932.

**Your Stock Market Losses** helps students understand the extent of the drop in stock prices between the highs of September 3, 1929, and the lows of October 29, 1929. Students calculate the value of a list of stocks on both those dates and then perform other calculations that reveal the danger of buying stocks on margin, as so many people did in 1929.

**Hooverisms** introduces students to the ironic American response to President Hoover's insistence that the country's problems were not really so bad. Students try to figure out what the listed optimistic "Hoover" terms really mean—for example, "Hoover hog" for a wild rabbit caught and cooked for food in place of pork. The Extra Challenges ask students to make up their own "Hooverisms" and explain what the verb "hoover" meant in the Finnish language in the 1920s, ironically related to Hoover's wartime work to fend off starvation in Belgium.

**Images of the Great Depression** presents photographs of people affected by the Depression. Students study the photographs and then use what they know about the Depression to write a narrative for at least one of the photos, telling the story behind the picture.

**The Life of Tenant Farmers** presents statements of African-American tenant farmers about the conditions of their lives in the rural South of the 1930s. Students role-play a family discussion about their dilemma as sharecroppers or tenant farmers and possible solutions to the situation.

**The Great Depression at Home** provides a series of suggestions to help students explore the effects of the Great Depression on their local community and create a class display to share what they learn.

**Women of the Thirties: In Real Life** invites students to give a thumbnail sketch of each of five 1930s women, from famous to notorious. **Women of the Thirties: On the Screen** invites students to identify four 1930s female screen stars and explain why each one appealed to Depression-era audiences.

# The Great Depression

## The Flaws in the Booming Economy

Many Americans enjoyed great prosperity during the 1920s. The boom times had happened under Republican presidents. So, it was no surprise when Republican Herbert Hoover won the 1928 election for U.S. president by a huge margin. But the economy had serious flaws. Not everyone was doing well.

Some U.S. industries were in trouble by the later 1920s. Mining, textiles, lumbering, and railroads saw falling profits and rising unemployment. Farmers had gone into debt during World War I to expand and take advantage of the high wartime demand. Now their markets had shrunk. Prices were down, but farmers' costs were up. Farms failed. Rural banks that had financed them failed, too.

Closed bank, Haverhill, Iowa

Workers' wages didn't rise much during the 1920s. But production of consumer goods did. By the late 1920s, manufacturers were producing more goods than people could afford to buy. Unsold goods piled up in warehouses. People went into debt by buying things on the installment plan. They agreed to make monthly payments for their purchases instead of paying all at once.

## The Stock Market and Its Crash

A big part of the economy of the late 1920s was the stock market. Prices of stocks had been rising steadily all through the decade. In the spring of 1928, an already strong New York stock market began rising rapidly. Everyone seemed to want part of the action. Even working-class and middle-class people had money in stocks.

Here's what happened during the stock boom: You could buy a stock one day, hold it for a few weeks or a month, and then sell it at a great profit. Then you could take your profit and repeat the process. On paper, you were making thousands or tens of thousands or hundreds of thousands of dollars. A lot of these stocks were bought "on margin." That is, the buyers paid only part of the price of the stocks at the time of purchase. The buyers would pay the rest of the purchase price when the stock was sold at a profit. It was foolproof! Prices would always keep going up—wouldn't they?

*(continued)*

# The Great Depression *(continued)*

During 1929, rising stock prices created a buying frenzy. People from all walks of life poured their life savings into the market. Then, suddenly, a wave of selling started on October 24, 1929. By the end of this Black Thursday, the market had dropped by $3 billion. The following Tuesday, the market plummeted again. Prices kept falling through November.

## The Great Depression Begins

The stock market crash signaled the start of the worst depression in the history of the United States. It was so bad that it was called the Great Depression. Factories closed. Millions of jobs disappeared. Banks failed. Businesses, large and small, collapsed. Foreign trade dried up as the Depression spread worldwide.

The Dust Bowl

The Great Depression hit Americans hard. People of all classes lost their life savings, their homes, their jobs, their incomes. By 1932, more than 13 million Americans were unemployed. Towns and cities across the nation opened soup kitchens. Bread lines formed everywhere. Hungry, jobless people lined up for meager free meals. Former bankers and teachers stood on city sidewalks selling apples for 5 cents apiece. Countless people became homeless. They could no longer pay their rent or make their house payments.

The situation was so bad that people became resigned instead of angry. People felt ashamed. They blamed themselves for their situation instead of the flawed economy. They lived in fear that things would get worse. They though they might never again be able to provide for themselves or their families.

## Social Life in the Depression

People needed relief from their problems during the Depression. Most people still did have homes. They gathered quietly at home with the family to play games. Contract bridge was popular. So was the new board game of Monopoly. Escape to other worlds via books and films was also very popular.

| Best-selling books of the 1930s: | Favorite movies of the 1930s: |
| --- | --- |
| *The Good Earth* by Pearl Buck, a saga of a Chinese peasant family<br>*Gone with the Wind* by Margaret Mitchell, a Civil War epic | *Monkey Business,* with the Marx Brothers<br>*Snow White,* Walt Disney cartoon<br>*The Wizard of Oz,* with Judy Garland<br>*King Kong,* with Fay Wray |

*(continued)*

# The Great Depression *(continued)*

In 1938, young actor Orson Welles broadcast a Halloween radio show based on H. G. Wells's novel *War of the Worlds*. The script began as a program of dance music. The music kept getting interrupted by "news reports" of an invasion by ruthless Martians armed with death rays. The reports said the creatures from Mars landed in New Jersey. ("Ladies and gentlemen, this is the most terrifying thing I have ever witnessed. . . . Wait a minute! Someone's *crawling out of the hollow top.*") Many terrified listeners missed the announcer's explanation that the broadcast wasn't real news. Panicked people piled into their cars. They clogged the highways of New Jersey trying to escape the menacing Martians. Americans across the country frantically called the police to find out how to save themselves and their families. It took several days for the commotion to die down.

## *The Hoover Response*

**Herbert Hoover**

The U.S. economy collapsed in the Great Depression. President Herbert Hoover responded with conventional remedies.

- He called for business leaders to keep up production, wages, and prices. They weren't able to.

- He kept the federal budget balanced. This meant there wasn't enough government spending to boost the sick economy.

- He gave government help to banks and businesses. He reasoned that their recovery would eventually help individual people.

- He believed that direct federal relief to people would undermine the essential American character of "rugged individualism." He left direct relief to voluntary efforts and private, local charity.

No one had experienced conditions like this before. Hoover believed his approach would get the economy up and running again. But the economic crisis was too extreme for Hoover's cautious policies to produce a recovery. Instead, the Depression grew worse. People became resentful of Hoover. They thought he didn't care about their plight. By 1932, that year's presidential election was the Democrats' for the taking. They nominated Franklin D. Roosevelt. He reversed Hoover's huge 1928 vote margin. A frontal assault on the Depression was about to be launched.

*Focus on U.S. History:*
*The Era of Modernization Through the 1930s*

# Your Economic Problems

Not everyone in the 1920s enjoyed boom times of prosperity. Imagine you are each of the people described below. How do the often overlooked problems with the economy of the 1920s affect your life? (These problems together helped to bring on the Great Depression.)

1. You are a coal miner in West Virginia. _____

   _____

2. You are an African-American sharecropper in Alabama. _____

   _____

3. You are a Nebraska wheat farmer. _____

   _____

4. You own a small manufacturing company that makes household appliances (stoves,

   refrigerators, washing machines). _____

   _____

5. You are a female garment worker in Massachusetts. _____

   _____

6. You are a blue-collar worker in the steel industry. _____

   _____

7. You are a loan officer at a rural bank in Kansas. _____

   _____

# Presidential Elections: 1928 and 1932

**Directions:** The maps below show state-by-state results of the 1928 and 1932 presidential elections. Look at the maps, and then answer the questions that follow.

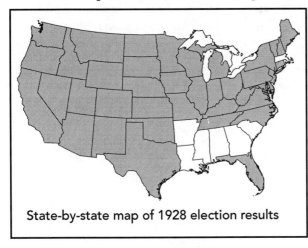

State-by-state map of 1928 election results

State-by-state map of 1932 election results

**1928: Popular vote/Electoral vote**
▨ Hoover: 21.4 million / 444
☐ Smith:  15 million   / 87

**1932: Popular vote/Electoral vote**
☐ Roosevelt: 22.8 million / 472
▨ Hoover:  15.8 million / 59

1. In 1928, why did the Democratic candidate carry primarily states in the Deep South? 

_____

2. In 1928, why did Hoover carry the rest of the states in the country? _____

_____

3. In 1932, why did Hoover lose almost all of the states he had carried in 1928? _____

_____

4. What change in party strength and regional voting does the 1932 map begin to show?

_____

_____

**Extra Challenge:** Study a chart of results for twentieth-century presidential elections. Look at figures for presidents who ran for reelection and lost. Then answer these questions:

5. Have any presidents lost as much support as Hoover did from 1928 to 1932?

6. What common result do presidents who have been reelected share?

7. What conclusion might you draw from this?

*Focus on U.S. History:*
*The Era of Modernization Through the 1930s*

# Your Stock Market Losses

**Directions:** The booming bull stock market hit a high on September 3, 1929. It crashed on October 24 (Black Thursday) and again on October 29, 1929. Suppose you were a typical small investor of that time. Shown below is your investment portfolio, with stock prices for both those high and low dates. You own 100 shares of each stock. How much did your total stock account gain or lose in value between September 3 and October 29? Fill in the values to find out.

| | Per share high on 9/3/29 | Value of 100 shares | Per share low on 10/29/29 | Value of 100 shares |
|---|---|---|---|---|
| Auburn Auto | 498 | _____ | 120 | _____ |
| Electric Auto-Lite | 154 | _____ | 50 | _____ |
| Brooklyn Union Gas | 247 | _____ | 100 | _____ |
| Purity Bakeries | $144\frac{3}{8}$ | _____ | 55 | _____ |
| Montgomery Ward | $137\frac{7}{8}$ | _____ | $49\frac{1}{2}$ | _____ |
| Radio Corporation | 101 | _____ | 26 | _____ |
| White Sewing Machine | $17\frac{7}{8}$ | _____ | 1 | _____ |
| | Total Value | _____ | | _____ |

Well, you lost a lot, didn't you? How much? _____ But you still *have* a fair amount, don't you? But wait—you bought the stocks on September 3 on margin—that is, you paid only 50 percent of the stock prices when you bought them. You owe your broker the balance. You expected to pay that balance by selling the stocks at a profit. Now your broker has called for the balance that you owe on the stock purchases. Can you pay, or are you hopelessly in debt? Show your figures here:

Total cost of the stock purchases on 9/3/29: _____

Balance that you owe to your broker (50%): _____

Current value of the stocks: _____

# Hooverisms

As the Great Depression deepened, President Herbert Hoover continued to insist that the country's problems were only temporary and not as bad as some people claimed. "Conditions are fundamentally sound," Hoover declared late in 1929. Americans with no jobs, little food, no homes, and no money responded with ironic humor. They renamed the marks of Depression poverty with optimistic "Hoover" terms.

**Directions:** See if you can determine what each of the following things really is. Write your answers on the lines.

1. Hoover hog: _____

2. Hoover flag: _____

3. Hoover blanket: _____

4. Hoover car: _____

5. Hoover bag: _____

6. Hoover shoes: _____

7. Hooverville: _____

Al Capone, the notorious Chicago gangster, set up and paid for a breadline to feed unemployed people in his city. When Capone attended Chicago baseball games, the crowd cheered him. President Hoover saw federal breadlines and said, "Nobody is actually starving. The hoboes, for example, are better fed than they have ever been." When Hoover threw out the first ball at a major-league baseball game, the crowd booed him.

**Extra Challenges:**

• With classmates, make up your own "Hooverisms" for marks of Depression-era poverty.

• During the 1920s, the word "hoover" entered into the Finnish language. What did it mean? Why?

*Focus on U.S. History:
The Era of Modernization Through the 1930s*

# Images of the Great Depression

During the Depression, the government (mainly the Farm Security Administration) paid talented photographers to record in pictures contemporary people's struggles. Here are some of those photographs.

**Directions:** Look closely at each picture on this page and the next. Notice details, such as the expressions on the people's faces, their clothing, their body language, their surroundings. Then write a narrative for at least one of these photographs, telling the story behind the picture. How did these people live before the Great Depression hit? What happened to them when hard times came? What brought them to the point captured in the photograph? Where do they go from here?

Eviction of black sharecroppers, Missouri, 1939

*(continued)*

# Images of the Great Depression *(continued)*

Oklahoma migrants

Sign man, New York City, 1937

# The Life of Tenant Farmers

**Directions:** Life for African-American tenant farmers and sharecroppers in the rural South was very hard. It got even harder during the Depression years. Here are some of the stories tenant farmers told to Charles Johnson, a black scholar and university professor.

Black sharecropper and family

◆ If it wasn't the boll weevil, it was the drought; if it wasn't the drought, it was the rains. . . . One thing, we ain't got proper tools we ought to have. If you git any good land you have to buy things to make it good, and that takes lots of money, and if we had money to buy these things we wouldn't be so hard up.

◆ Ain't make nothing, don't speck nothing no more till I die.

◆ I know we been beat out of money direct and indirect. You see, they got a chance to do it all right, 'cause they can overcharge us and I know it's being done. I made three bales again last year. He said I owed $400 the beginning of the year. Now you can't dispute his word. When I said 'Suh?' he said 'Don't you dispute my word; the book says so.' . . .You better take to the bushes too if you dispute him, for he will string you up for that. I just have to take what they say, 'cause I don't want to go to the mines [prison labor] and I do want to live.

◆ I tried keeping books one year, and the man kept worrying me about it, saying his books was the ones he went by anyhow. . . . They got you 'cause you have to carry your cotton to his mill to gin and you better not carry your cotton nowhere else. I don't care how good your cotton is, a colored man's cotton is always second- or third-grade cotton if a colored man sells it. The only way you can get first prices for it is to get some white man to sell it for you in his name. . . . See, when a fella's got a gun in your face you gotter take low or die.

**Directions:** Role-play a family discussion about the dilemma you are in as tenant farmers or share-croppers. You are always in debt to the white people who own the land you farm and the mill that gins your cotton and the store where you buy your supplies. Is there any way out of this trap? Should you leave and move to the North? Can you do that? If you stay, how can you make a decent living?

Excerpts from *The Shadow of the Plantation* by Charles S. Johnson (Chicago: University of Chicago Press).
Copyright 1934 by the University of Chicago. All Rights Reserved.

Name _____

Date _____

# The Great Depression at Home

**Directions:** Explore the effects of the Great Depression on your local community. Gather information from local sources, using the suggestions below as a guide. Use the information you gather to create a class display supported by written materials. Design your display to share what you've learned with fellow students and members of the community in an interesting, visually engaging, and informative way.

*People to Interview:*

Family members
Friends and relatives of your friends
Long-time community residents
Bankers, business owners

*Local History Sources:*

Community libraries
Local historical societies
Local newspapers

*Visual Materials for the Display:*

Photographs—homes, businesses, farms—before, during, after the Depression
Photocopies of local and national news stories of the Depression era
Memorabilia from the 1930s

*Specific Information to Investigate:*

Personal experiences (Sample interview questions: How did the Depression years affect you and your family? Did you/they lose a job, a home, a business, a farm? Did you need or accept any assistance? When did the hard times end for you and your family?)

Effects of the Depression on local businesses, banks, and farms

Sources of help in the local area during the Depression (For example, were any WPA or CCC projects undertaken in your community? Did local soup kitchens open?)

Local results in the presidential campaigns of 1928, 1932, and 1936

# Women of the Thirties: In Real Life

**Directions:** Women of the Great Depression had some interesting famous females to relate to—or disassociate from. Can you give a thumbnail sketch of each of these thirties women?

Babe Didrickson Zaharias, jumping hurdles

◆ **Eleanor Roosevelt** _____

_____

_____

_____

◆ **Frances Perkins** _____

_____

_____

_____

◆ **Mary McLeod Bethune** _____

_____

_____

_____

◆ **Babe Didrickson Zaharias** _____

_____

_____

_____

◆ **Bonnie Parker** _____

_____

_____

_____

*Focus on U.S. History:*
*The Era of Modernization Through the 1930s*

# Women of the Thirties: On the Screen

**Directions:** People flocked to the movies in the thirties to get away from their problems. Who were each of these 1930s female screen stars? What about each one appealed to Depression-era audiences? Which one(s) are real, and which ones are fictional?

Saturday night, Iowa Falls, Iowa, 1939

◆ **Scarlett O'Hara**

_____

_____

_____

_____

◆ **Shirley Temple**

_____

_____

_____

_____

◆ **Snow White**

_____

_____

_____

_____

◆ **Ginger Rogers**

_____

_____

_____

_____

*Focus on U.S. History:*
*The Era of Modernization Through the 1930s*

# The New Deal

The objective of this unit is to guide students to an understanding of the ways in which the New Deal addressed the Great Depression and initiated the modern welfare state. Demoralized Americans elected Franklin D. Roosevelt in 1932 on his promise of a "new deal," a new way for the United States to attack and end the Great Depression. Roosevelt delivered on the promise with a flurry of New Deal programs, including numerous new federal agencies. Banks, businesses, and stock transactions became subject to many new federal regulations. New federal programs helped farmers, blue-collar workers, unem-ployed people, artists and writers, students, elderly and disabled Americans, rural and urban alike. While many people supported Roosevelt's New Deal, the Supreme Court took a dim view of it until late in the 1930s, and alternative plans promoted by such people as Huey Long and Father Coughlin attracted much support. By the time the New Deal wound down in the late 1930s, it had transformed the size and role of government in American life. This unit's activities are designed to draw students into a better understanding of the New Deal and the tremendous changes it created in the United States.

# Student Activities

**"Nothing to Fear . . ."** presents excerpts from Roosevelt's important first inaugural address, which reassured the demoralized American people and sparked both individual Americans and the Congress to action. Students imagine themselves as specific 1930s Americans (students, bankers, factory workers, and so on) and role-play a discussion about their reaction to the speech. **Hoover vs. Roosevelt** gives some of Herbert Hoover's negative reaction to Roosevelt's "new deal" plan. Students can use Hoover's viewpoint in their role-play response to the Roosevelt speech.

**Presidential Campaigns, 1900–1932**, gives a variety of campaign slogans from presidential elections. Students match each slogan with the correct campaign.

**TR and FDR** provides a framework for students to compare aspects of the lives of Theodore Roosevelt and Franklin D. Roosevelt, who were distant cousins. Students will discover that the lives of these two U.S. presidents shared a remarkable number of similarities.

**What Is It? A New Deal Game** strengthens students' familiarity with New Deal programs by having teams quiz each other on the function of New Deal agencies and laws. The Extra Challenge asks students to identify which of these agencies are still in existence today and which, if any, offer services that would be available to students and their families.

**You and the New Deal** puts students into the shoes of specific Americans and has them tell what part of the New Deal might have helped them in their particular situation.

**Be a New Deal Worker** has each student become an unemployed person in the 1930s and write a job application for one (or more) of the listed government-sponsored New Deal jobs, relating her or his interests and skills to the position(s) chosen.

**Share Our Wealth** presents Senator Huey Long's Share-Our-Wealth proposal. Students evaluate Long's plan in a discussion with classmates, considering the plan in the context both of the 1930s and of today.

**No New Deal!** gives thumbnail sketches of other well-known opponents of the Roosevelt program. Students give a summary of the plan each man— Upton Sinclair, Father Charles Coughlin, and Dr. Francis E. Townsend—proposed to pull the nation out of the Great Depression. The Extra Challenge asks students to give more details about each plan, and to evaluate each one.

**The Supreme Court and the New Deal** presents brief excerpts from two Supreme Court decisions, one ruling against a minimum wage in 1923 and another upholding a minimum wage in 1937. Students compare the reasoning in the two decisions. The Extra Challenge asks students to relate the two decisions to the changing attitude of the Supreme Court toward New Deal legislation.

**FDR and the Supreme Court** examines FDR's "court-packing" plan. It presents Roosevelt's declaration of the two chief purposes of his plan and a cartoon showing one view of public and congressional reaction to the plan. Questions guide students through a look at constitutional provisions for the Supreme Court, Roosevelt's plan, and the public reaction. The Extra Challenge asks students to create their own editorial cartoon about Roosevelt's court plan or to write an editorial or a letter to the editor about it.

**The New Deal Time Line** lists important milestones in the New Deal era and asks students to create a time line with dates and descriptions of the events.

Name _____

Date _____

# The New Deal

## FDR and His "New Deal"

Americans went to the polls in 1932 to elect a president. Voters firmly rejected the failed policies of Republican Herbert Hoover. Instead, they elected Democrat Franklin D. Roosevelt. When Roosevelt accepted the nomination for president, he had declared, "I pledge you, I pledge myself, to a new deal for the American people." No one, least of all Roosevelt, knew exactly what programs and policies the New Deal would include. But the very prospect of *some* bold government action gave people hope. So did Roosevelt's confident manner.

**Franklin D. Roosevelt**

At the beginning, the New Deal was more a state of mind than a specific plan. Roosevelt said, "The country needs bold, persistent experimentation. It is common sense to take a method and try it. If it fails, admit it frankly and try another. But above all, try something." Demoralized Americans agreed.

## The First Hundred Days

In his inauguration speech, FDR reassured Americans and called for action. The people responded gladly. So did Congress. It quickly passed a barrage of New Deal laws proposed by Roosevelt. This flurry of lawmaking was known as the Hundred Days. It revived national confidence. Here are some of the things that happened during the Hundred Days:

- Closed banks reopened, with government support.
- Bank deposits became insured by the U.S. government.
- A federal emergency relief agency gave out over $1 billion in grants. The money went to states, local governments, and private charities.

- Federal works agencies hired millions of unemployed people for much-needed public works projects. The new workers tackled public needs like building and repairing roads, bridges, schools, and sewers.
- Legions of unmarried young men worked outdoors in federal conservation projects.
- Major industries drew up and followed fair business codes.
- Farmers received payments for *not* planting crops. Farm surpluses went down, and farm prices went up.

*(continued)*

*Focus on U.S. History:*
*The Era of Modernization Through the 1930s*

# The New Deal *(continued)*

## The Second Hundred Days

Some people thought the New Deal didn't do enough. Others thought it went too far. Roosevelt saw that his moderate New Deal approach had not gained much business or conservative support. People who did support reform, including Congress, wanted more. So Roosevelt launched what was called the "Second Hundred Days." The main parts of the First Hundred Days had tried to regulate business and plan the economy. The Second Hundred Days focused more on setting up a governmental safety net for U.S. citizens. It included the following:

- Unemployment insurance, old-age pensions, and support for disabled persons
- The right of workers to bargain through unions
- Electric lines for homes throughout rural America
- Higher taxes on large incomes and inheritances
- Federal jobs for writers, visual artists, theater people, and musicians.

The presidential election of 1936 was a nationwide referendum on the New Deal. Roosevelt won in a landslide, losing only two states (Maine and Vermont). He had drawn his votes from the classes of people most helped by New Deal programs. They were workers (both union and nonunion), minorities, the underprivileged, city dwellers, and farmers, plus traditional southern Democrats.

## The New Deal and the American People

Women gained new status in government during the New Deal. First Lady Eleanor Roosevelt was a very visible social activist. Frances Perkins was the first female Cabinet member in U.S. history. Mrs. Roosevelt and other Democratic women developed an informal network. Women in key posts drew other reform-minded women into New Deal government jobs.

**Eleanor Roosevelt**

In the 1936 election, African Americans voted in large numbers for Roosevelt. They didn't gain a lot under the New Deal, however. Many New Deal programs did not treat blacks and whites equally. The programs paid blacks less, hired blacks less often, even segregated black workers. However, many African Americans did benefit to some extent from New Deal programs. And the Roosevelts brought African Americans into high-level government posts. Mary McCleod Bethune, Charles Forman, and others formed a "Black Cabinet." They lobbied and advised on policies and opportunities that affected black Americans.

*(continued)*

# The New Deal (continued)

Farm workers (hired hands, not farm owners) received little help from the New Deal. The Social Security Act didn't apply to them. So, Southern black sharecroppers weren't much better off during the New Deal than they had been before. Neither were Mexican-American laborers in the Southwest.

Native American policy during the New Deal changed. It had focused on assimilation into white culture. Now it shifted to an emphasis on tribal government and tribal cultures. Native Americans had mixed reactions to this.

When the Depression began, only a small percentage of workers belonged to labor unions. These unions were mostly for skilled workers. In 1936, John Lewis and other labor leaders formed the Congress of Industrial Organizations. The CIO worked hard to form unions among mass-production workers in the steel and auto industries. The craft unions had excluded African Americans. The CIO welcomed them and other minorities. The Wagner Act of 1935 protected many of the CIO's organizing activities.

## The End of the New Deal

In 1935, the U.S. Supreme Court began striking down New Deal laws. The Court found that the laws were in conflict with the U.S. Constitution. An angry FDR proposed adding up to six judges to the Court. The proposal, in turn, got the American public and Congress angry. They didn't want politics to interfere with the federal courts. Although the Court-packing idea didn't work, the Court did change its mind about New Deal laws. It upheld the Wagner Act and Social Security. Soon Roosevelt was able to fill empty Court posts with New-Deal-minded judges.

The backlash against Roosevelt about the Court eroded some of the president's power. A brief "Roosevelt recession" in 1937–38 did, too. Congress was no longer willing to pass New Deal laws. The program wound down as the economy slowly moved toward recovery.

The New Deal was extremely important in U.S. history. It didn't completely end the Depression. It didn't help everyone in need. But it changed the role and size of government in American life. For the first time, government took on a broad role of protecting the basic well-being of its citizens. It would keep the needy, the disabled, the aged, the out-of-work from extreme want. And for the first time, the American people looked to the government to provide this kind of help. The federal government had become a part of most people's lives—for better or worse.

Unemployment office, Pittsburgh, PA, 1938

# Hoover vs. Roosevelt

In the presidential election of 1932, Franklin D. Roosevelt proposed a "new deal" for the Depression economy. He outlined his ideas for this "new deal" in his inaugural address on March 4, 1933. It was the speech that launched him as president of the United States. Here are parts of this famous speech.

**Franklin D. Roosevelt, inaugural speech, 1933**

[F]irst of all, let me assert my firm belief that the only thing we have to fear is fear itself—nameless, unreasoning, unjustified terror which paralyzes needed efforts to convert retreat into advance. In every dark hour of our national life a leadership of frankness and vigor has met with that understanding and support of the people themselves which is essential to victory. I am convinced that you will again give that support to leadership in these critical days.

In such a spirit on my part and on yours we face our common difficulties. They concern, thank God, only material things. Values have shrunken to fantastic levels; taxes have risen; our ability to pay has fallen; government of all kinds is faced by serious curtailment of income; the means of exchange are frozen in the currents of trade; the withered leaves of industrial enterprise lie on every side; farmers find no markets for their produce; the savings of many years in thousands of families are gone.

More important, a host of unemployed citizens face the grim problem of existence, and an equally great number toil with little return. Only a foolish optimist can deny the dark realities of the moment.

Yet our distress comes from no failure of substance. We are stricken by no plague of locusts. . . . We still have much to be thankful for. Nature still offers her bounty, and human efforts have multiplied it. Plenty is at our doorstep, but a generous use of it languishes in the very sight of the supply. Primarily this is because the [financial and big-business leaders] have failed, through their own stubbornness and their own incompetence.

. . . Faced by the failure of credit, they have proposed only the lending of more money. . . . They have resorted to exhortations, pleading tearfully for restored confidence. They know only the rules of a generation of self-seekers. They have no vision, and when there is no vision the people perish. . . . This nation asks for action, and action now.

Our greatest primary task is to put people to work. This is no unsolvable problem if we face it wisely and courageously. It can be accomplished in part by direct recruiting by the government itself, treating the task as we would treat the emergency of a war, but, at the same time, through this employment, accomplishing greatly needed projects to stimulate and reorganize the use of our natural resources.

*(continued)*

# Hoover vs. Roosevelt *(continued)*

Hand in hand with this we must [reorganize and direct the economy]. The task can be helped by definite efforts to raise the values of agricultural products and with this the power to purchase the output of our cities. It can be helped by preventing realistically the tragedy of the growing loss through foreclosure of our small homes and our farms. It can be helped by insistence that the federal, state, and local governments act forthwith on the demand that their cost be drastically reduced. It can be helped by the unifying of relief activities which today are often scattered, uneconomical, and unequal. It can be helped by national planning for and supervision of all forms of transportation and of communications and other utilities which have a definitely public character. There are many ways in which it can be helped, but it can never be helped merely by talking about it. We must act and act quickly.

Finally, in our progress toward a resumption of work, we require two safeguards against a return of the evils of the old order: there must be a strict supervision of all banking and credits and investments; there must be an end to speculation with other people's money, and there must be provision for an adequate but sound currency.

These are the lines of attack. I shall presently urge upon a new Congress in special session detailed measures for their fulfillment. . . .

If I read the temper of our people correctly, we now realize as we have never realized before our interdependence on each other; that we cannot merely take but we must give as well; that if we are to go forward, we must move as a trained and loyal army willing to sacrifice for the good of a common discipline, because without such discipline no progress is made, no leadership becomes effective.

. . . I assume unhesitatingly the leadership of this great army of our people dedicated to a disciplined attack upon our common problems.

Herbert Hoover disagreed with Roosevelt's proposals. Here is some of what Hoover had to say about Roosevelt's "new deal" plan.

### Herbert Hoover, 1932

This campaign is more than a contest between two men. It is more than a contest between two parties. It is a contest between two philosophies of government.

We are told by the opposition that we must have a change, that we must have a new deal. It is not the change that comes from normal development of national life to which I object but the proposal to alter the whole foundations of our national life which have been builded through generations of testing and struggle, and of the principles upon which we have builded the nation. . . .

*(continued)*

# Hoover vs. Roosevelt *(continued)*

Our economic system has received abnormal shocks during the past three years, which temporarily dislocated its normal functioning. These shocks have in a large sense come from without our borders, but I say to you that our system of government has enabled us to take such strong action as to prevent the disaster which would otherwise have come to our nation. It has enabled us further to develop measures and programs which are now demonstrating their ability to bring about restoration and progress. . . .

[Our American system] is founded on the conception that only through ordered liberty, through freedom to the individual, and equal opportunity to the individual will his initiative and enterprise be summoned to spur the march of progress. . . .

This freedom of the individual creates of itself the necessity and the cheerful willingness of men to act cooperatively in a thousand ways and for every purpose as occasion arises. . . . It is in the further development of this cooperation and a sense of its responsibility that we should find solution for many of our complex problems, and not by the extension of government into our economic and social life. The greatest function of government is to build up that cooperation, and its most resolute action should be to deny the extension of bureaucracy.

. . . [Our American system] is founded upon the conception of responsibility of the individual to the community, of the responsibility of local government to the state, of the state to the national government. . . . The centralization of government will undermine responsibilities and will destroy the system.

**Directions:** Imagine yourself back in the 1930s. You have just listened to FDR's inaugural speech. What do you think of it? What effect does it have on you? Consider this from the point of view of a number of different people—a farmer, a banker, a business owner, a housewife, a coal miner, a factory worker, a stockbroker, a teacher, a high school or college student, a Republican, a Democrat, and so on. Does Hoover's anti-New Deal perspective change the effect Roosevelt's speech has? Role-play a discussion of the speech with classmates, with each student assuming a different Depression-era identity. Use the points Hoover makes to help with the negative side of your role-play discussion.

# Presidential Campaigns, 1900–1932

**Directions:** Match these slogans of presidential election campaigns with the candidate and year they belong with. Write the letter of the campaign next to the appropriate slogan.

_____ 1. "The Full Dinner Pail"

_____ 2. "The Square Deal"

_____ 3. "He kept us out of war."

_____ 4. "The New Deal"

_____ 5. "Keep Cool."

_____ 6. "New Freedom"

_____ 7. "Normalcy"

_____ 8. "New Nationalism"

_____ 9. "Prosperity is right around the corner."

_____ 10. "A chicken in every pot, a car in every garage."

(a) McKinley campaign, 1900

(b) Theodore Roosevelt campaign, 1904

(c) Theodore Roosevelt campaign, 1912

(d) Wilson campaign, 1912

(e) Wilson campaign, 1916

(f) Harding campaign, 1920

(g) Coolidge campaign, 1924

(h) Hoover campaign, 1928

(i) Hoover campaign, 1932

(j) Franklin D. Roosevelt campaign, 1932

# TR and FDR

**Directions:** Theodore Roosevelt and Franklin D. Roosevelt were distant cousins. (Franklin's wife Eleanor was also related—she was Theodore's niece.) They were the products of different times and belonged to different political parties. Were they at all alike? Fill in the table below to find out.

| | **Theodore Roosevelt** | **Franklin D. Roosevelt** |
|---|---|---|
| family background | | |
| health/illness | | |
| college he graduated from | | |
| first elected state office | | |
| highest elected state office | | |
| high-level appointive federal office in Washington, DC | | |
| first national office campaigned for (and the outcome) | | |
| political party | | |
| political philosophy | | |
| attitude toward being president of the U.S. | | |

# What Is It? A New Deal Game

**Directions:** Form teams, cut out these cards, and play a New Deal What Is It? game. Teams take turns drawing cards and reading aloud the name of the New Deal agency or law on that card. Opposing teams tell what the purpose of that agency was.

| | |
|---|---|
| **National Recovery Administration (NRA)** <br><br> Took charge of drawing up and supervising the operation of codes of fair business practices for individual industries. | **Civilian Conservation Corps (CCC)** <br><br> Provided jobs for single young men in reforestation and other conservation projects. |
| **Public Works Administration (PWA)** <br><br> Paid people to work on public works projects (e.g., building and repairing roads, dams, tunnels, public buildings, hospitals, etc.) | **Works Progress Administration (WPA)** <br><br> Paid people to work on public works; also paid artists, theater people, writers to paint, sculpt, put on performances, write, and so on. |
| **Federal Deposit Insurance Corp. (FDIC)** <br><br> Guaranteed bank deposits for the depositors. | **Home Owners Loan Corp. (HOLC)** <br><br> Refinanced mortgages and prevented foreclosures. |
| **Federal Securities Act** <br><br> Required full financial information about new stock issues. | **Securities & Exchange Commission (SEC)** <br><br> Regulated stock sales. |

*(continued)*

# What Is It? A New Deal Game *(continued)*

| | |
|---|---|
| **Agricultural Adjustment Administration (AAA)** <br><br><br><br> Paid farmers to take part of their land out of cultivation. | **Tennessee Valley Authority (TVA)** <br><br><br><br> Built dams, power plants, and electric lines; sold electricity and fertilizer. |
| **Federal Emergency Relief Administration (FERA)** <br><br><br><br> Gave $500 million in emergency aid to the states. | **National Youth Administration (NYA)** <br><br><br><br> Created part-time jobs for more than 2 million high school and college students. |
| **National Labor Relations Board (NLRB)** <br><br><br><br> Supervised union elections, union/company bargaining, and employer practices. | **Social Security Administration** <br><br><br><br> Ran a new system of old-age insurance, plus coverage for widows, dependent children, and disabled workers. |
| **Rural Electrification Administration (REA)** <br><br><br><br> Loaned money at low interest rates to groups that would bring electrical lines to rural America. | **Soil Conservation Program** <br><br><br><br> Paid farmers not to plant crops that depleted the soil. |

*(continued)*

# What Is It? A New Deal Game (continued)

| | |
|---|---|
| **Farm Credit Administration**<br><br><br><br>Refinanced farm mortgages. | **Resettlement Administration**<br><br><br><br>Moved farmers from worn-out farms to better lands. |
| **Farm Security Administration**<br><br><br><br>Gave low-interest loans to help tenant farmers buy family farms. | **Federal Housing Administration (FHA)**<br><br><br><br>Gave low-cost loans to build new buildings and renovate old ones. |
| **Commodity Credit Corporation**<br><br><br><br>Gave loans to farmers who stored crops rather than selling them. | **Revenue Act of 1935 (Wealth Tax Act)**<br><br><br><br>Taxed high incomes and inheritances. |
| **Banking Act of 1935**<br><br><br><br>Gave Federal Reserve Board control of the money market (interest rates, money supply). | **Public Utilities Holding Company Act of 1935**<br><br><br><br>Limited the size of utility companies and allowed for federal regulation of utility rates. |

**Extra Challenge:** Which of these agencies are still in existence today? Are any of their services available to you and your family?

# You and the New Deal

**Directions:** How would the New Deal have affected you? Think about this by imagining you are each of the people described below. What part of the New Deal might have helped you in your situation?

1. You are a farmer in a rural area, struggling with debt and low crop prices.

2. You are a middle-class office manager who can't make your mortgage payments and lost all your savings in banks.

3. You are a young person out of a job.

4. You are a factory worker with very low wages, no union, and poor working conditions.

5. You lost a bundle in the stock market.

6. You are a poor "starving" artist.

7. You are a 60-year-old person about to lose your job and with no savings or pension plan.

*Focus on U.S. History:*
*The Era of Modernization Through the 1930s*

# Be a New Deal Worker

So many people were out of work during the Great Depression that the New Deal included federal work programs. All kinds of unemployed people—skilled, unskilled, semi-skilled—could find a job set up and run by the government. They earned paychecks issued by the government.

**Directions:** Suppose you are out of work in the 1930s. Which of these government-sponsored jobs would you want to take and why? (You can choose multiple jobs, if you want to.) Write a paragraph for a job application that relates your interests and skills to the project(s) you want to work on.

*Jobs with the CCC:*

- planting trees in national forests
- restoring historic battlegrounds
- maintaining trails and campsites at national parks
- working on flood control and soil erosion projects

*Jobs with the PWA and WPA:*

- building Boulder Dam in Colorado
- building the Triborough Bridge or the Lincoln Tunnel in New York City
- creating the Mall in Washington, DC
- constructing a school building or hospital
- taking part in a federal arts program:
  painting murals in public buildings (e.g., post offices, libraries, courthouses)
  writing state guide books
  recording people's oral histories
  acting, directing, doing stagehand work in Federal Theatre Project shows

_____

_____

_____

_____

_____

_____

Workers in the Civilian Conservation Corps (CCC) were called the Soil Soldiers and Roosevelt's Tree Army.

The CCC was only for young men. People who objected to that asked, "Where's the she, she, she in the CCC?"

# Share Our Wealth

Louisiana Senator Huey Long ("the Kingfish") didn't think much of Franklin Roosevelt's New Deal. Long developed his own plan to fight the Great Depression. He called it the Share Our Wealth program. Here are the plan's main points.

**Huey Long's Share Our Wealth proposal, 1935**

**Huey Long**

1. The fortunes of the multimillionaires and billionaires shall be reduced so that no one person shall own more than a few million dollars to the person. We would do this by a capital levy tax. . . .

2. We propose to limit the amount any one man can earn in one year or inherit to $1 million to the person.

3. Now, by limiting the size of the fortunes and incomes of the big men, we will throw into the government Treasury the money and property from which we will care for the millions of people who have nothing; and with this money we will provide a home and the comforts of home, with such common conveniences as radio and automobile, for every family in America, free of debt.

4. We guarantee food and clothing and employment for everyone who should work by shortening the hours of labor to thirty hours per week, maybe less. We would have the hours shortened just so much as would give work to everybody to produce enough for everybody. . . .

5. We would provide education at the expense of the states and the United States for every child, not only through grammar school and high school but through to a college and vocational education. . . .

6. We would give a pension to all persons above sixty years of age in an amount sufficient to support them in comfortable circumstances, excepting those who earn $1,000 per year or who are worth $10,000. . . .

And now you have our program, none too big, none too little, but every man a king.

**Directions:** Evaluate Long's plan in a discussion with classmates. What real problem did Long's plan address? To help with your evaluation, frame the plan in today's terms. (How many millions would any one person be allowed to have today under this plan? How much could any one person earn in a year or inherit? What "comforts of home" would be included today?) Could such a plan work, in the 1930s or today? Who would be most likely to support a Share Our Wealth plan?

# No New Deal!

**Directions:** Franklin Roosevelt had other opponents besides Huey Long. They too developed their own plans. Read the descriptions of the anti-New Deal leaders below. Find out about the plan each man proposed to pull the nation out of the Great Depression. Then give a summary of each plan.

---

**Upton Sinclair:** A novelist and a socialist, he became the Democratic party's candidate for governor of California. He campaigned for a plan he called "End Poverty in California," or EPIC. Sinclair didn't win the election, but he did get a million votes.

Sinclair's economic plan: _____

_____

_____

---

**Father Charles Coughlin:** Known as the "Radio Priest," he attracted 30 to 45 million listeners to his weekly radio broadcasts from the Shrine of the Little Flower in Detroit. He founded the National Union for Social Justice to promote his plan. He received $500,000 a year in contributions.

Coughlin's economic plan: _____

_____

_____

---

**Dr. Francis E. Townsend:** A quiet California doctor retired from the public health service, he was very concerned about the plight of elderly Americans. Townsend Clubs sprang up all over the country, and 200,000 copies of the *Townsend National Weekly* went out to readers.

Townsend's economic plan: _____

_____

_____

---

**Extra Challenge:** For each plan, do the following: (a) Tell what real problem each plan tried to address. (b) Tell who tended to support each man and his plan. (c) Evaluate each plan.

# The Supreme Court and the New Deal

The U.S. Supreme Court ruled against important New Deal legislation. Later, it ruled in favor of types of laws it had previously ruled against. Here are two different Supreme Court decisions on minimum wages.

Supreme Court, Washington, D.C.

### *Adkins* v. *Children's Hospital,* 1923

To the extent that the sum fixed [the minimum wage] exceeds the fair value of the services rendered, it amounts to a compulsory exaction from the employer for the support of a partially indigent person, for whose condition there rests upon him [the employer] no peculiar responsibility, and therefore, in effect, arbitrarily shifts to his [the employer's] shoulders a burden which, if it belongs to anybody, belongs to society as a whole.

### *West Coast Hotel Co.* v. *Parrish,* 1937

The exploitation of a class of workers who are in an unequal position with respect to bargaining power and are thus relatively defenseless against the denial of a living wage is not only detrimental to their health and well being but casts a direct burden for their support upon the community. What these workers lose in wages the taxpayers are called upon to pay. The bare cost of living must be met.

**Directions:** Compare the reasoning in these two decisions. Whose responsibility is it to provide the minimum wage needed to live on? How did the Court's reasoning change from *Adkins* to *Parrish*?

**Extra Challenge:** Explain how these two decisions reflect the Supreme Court's (and society's) attitude toward the government's role before and after the Court began to accept New Deal legislation.

# FDR and the Supreme Court

The U.S. Supreme Court declared a number of important early New Deal laws unconstitutional. Frustrated by this, President Roosevelt proposed a plan to add up to six new justices to the Court. Below on the left are some of FDR's comments to the American people about his plan. Below on the right is a cartoon expressing the common reaction to FDR's "court-packing" plan.

**Directions:** Read Roosevelt's words, study the cartoon, and answer the following questions.

[My] plan has two chief purposes: By bringing into the judicial system a steady and continuing stream of new and younger blood, I hope, first, to make the administration of all Federal justice speedier and therefore less costly; secondly, to bring to the decision of social and economic problems younger men who have had personal experience and contact with modern facts and circumstances under which average men have to live and work. This plan will save our national Constitution from hardening of the judicial arteries.

1. What provisions for the Supreme Court are set by the U.S. Constitution? Read Article III of the Constitution to find out.

2. How would Roosevelt's plan change the Supreme Court?

3. What was the reaction to Roosevelt's plan, as shown in the cartoon? Why did the plan cause such a strong reaction? What specific objections did opponents of the plan have?

**Extra Challenge:** Create your own editorial cartoon about Roosevelt's court-packing plan. Or write an editorial or letter to the editor about the plan and Roosevelt's reasons for proposing it.

# The New Deal Time Line

**Directions:** With classmates, construct a time line for these important milestones in the New Deal era. Include a brief description of each. Illustrations would make your time line more interesting. Add to your time line the agencies and the dates they were started from your What Is It? New Deal game.

- Crash of N.Y. stock market
- Bonus Army march
- Franklin Roosevelt elected
- Roosevelt inaugurated
- Nationwide bank holiday
- Hundred Days
- Repeal of Eighteenth Amendment
- Dust Bowl storms begin
- American Liberty League founded
- Townsend Clubs sprout
- Indian Reorganization Act
- Father Coughlin creates National Union for Social Justice
- Huey Long creates Share Our Wealth Society
- Harlem race riot
- *Schechter Poultry Corp.* v. *U.S.*
- Second Hundred Days
- Long assassinated
- Boulder Dam built
- *Moorhead* v. *Tipaldo*
- Roosevelt reelected
- *Butler* v. *U.S.*
- CIO formed
- Sit-down strikes
- *N.L.R.B.* v. *Jones & Laughlin Steel Corp.*
- Roosevelt court-packing plan
- Roosevelt recession
- Fair Labor Standards Act
- Marian Anderson sings at the Lincoln Memorial
- World War II begins in Europe

Dust Bowl scene

*Focus on U.S. History:*
*The Era of Modernization Through the 1930s*

# ANSWERS, ADDITIONAL ACTIVITIES, AND ASSESSMENTS

## Unit 1: The Progressive Era

### Worksheet 1: Death of a President (page 6)

Other assassinations include Presidents Lincoln, Garfield, and Kennedy, Robert F. Kennedy, Martin Luther King, Jr., and Malcolm X. Examples of colorful and emotional language in the McKinley article include "that spirit of geniality the American people so well know," "with the leap of a tiger," and "so thrilling in its intensity."

### Worksheet 2: Reform Movements (page 8)

| Movement | Main issue or concern | Main reform organization(s) | Major leader(s) | Main accomplishment(s), 1900–1920 |
|---|---|---|---|---|
| temperance | ban on manufacture & sale of alcoholic beverages | Anti-Saloon League, Women's Christian Temperance Union (WCTU) | Carrie Nation | Eighteenth Amendment, ratified 1919 |
| child labor | regulating, limiting employment of children | National Child Labor Committee | Florence Kelley | passage of child labor reform laws in most states; Child Labor Act of 1916; Children's Bureau of the Dept. of Labor, 1912 |
| socialism | govt. control of industries, for benefit of workers/the people | Socialist Party of America | Eugene V. Debs | contributed to national debate on government's role in reform, offered more radical solutions |
| women's suffrage | getting women the right to vote, at federal and state levels | National Woman Suffrage Assn., National Woman's Party | Carrie Chapman Catt, Alva Belmont, Alice Paul | state voting rights; Nineteenth Amendment, ratified 1920 |
| radical labor | to abolish capitalism and "the wage system" | Industrial Workers of the World (IWW) | William "Big Bill" Haywood | few long-term accomplishments—led some successful strikes |
| black rights | eliminate racial inequality and discrimination | NAACP (National Association for the Advancement of Colored People) | W. E. B. DuBois | few results in Progressive era |
| anarchism | elimination of government | none | Emma Goldman | none |

## Worksheet 3: Reforming Government and Politics (page 9)

After students complete the activity sheets, you could assign students—individually or in groups—to research and report on which of these Progressive-era reforms is part of the political system in your city/town and state.

1. Initiative: What—system by which popular petition can present a bill to the legislature for action; Improvement—people can force state legislators to address issues the legislature might otherwise refuse to consider.

2. Recall: What—removal of elected officials by the voters; Improvement—voters can eject elected officials who are corrupt or who ignore the voters' best interests and/or wishes.

3. Referendum: What—method by which the people can vote to enact or repeal laws, bypassing the legislature; Improvement—an instance of direct democracy that gives people the power to take action the legislature might not take.

4. Citywide elections: What—city government leaders elected by all voters in the city, not by voters in individual wards; Improvement—breaks power of bosses in wards.

5. Secret ballot: What—voters mark ballots privately instead of casting ballots in front of voting officials and party politicians; Improvement—party bosses can no longer intimidate voters at polling places into voting for bosses and their candidates.

6. Direct primary: What—candidates for elective office are chosen by the voters; Improvement—the people, not the party bosses, choose candidates.

7. City manager: What—a commission or a city's councilors hire a professional city manager to run city government; Improvement—day-to-day city affairs are directed by a nonpartisan professional manager.

8. "Gas and water socialism": What—city takes over public utilities, runs them as part of the city government; Improvement—public utilities are run at cost, not for profit.

## Worksheet 4: Upton Sinclair, Muckraker (page 11)

1. Meat Inspection Act

2. Pure Food and Drug Act

You can access the full text of *The Jungle* on the Internet at http://sunsite.berkeley.edu/Literature/Sinclair/The Jungle/.

## Worksheet 6: Women and Work (page 14)

1. harm caused to others: Non-poor working women take needed work away from poor women and men; they take jobs that men need, or make men's wages lower, to the point that men don't earn enough to marry and support a family.

2. damage to marriage prospects: Men with lower wages because of working women can't afford to marry; working women lose the "grace and refined allurements of femininity" that men want in a wife; men always prefer a "home girl" to any other kind for a wife; working women mar their beauty, ruin their health, and lose their innocence, all of which men want in a wife.

3. moral harm: Working in factories endangers a woman's chastity.

4. health harm: Most working women suffer from nervous collapse and are doomed to bad health.

5. harm to "womanliness": Some or many types of jobs make women "bold, fierce, muscular, brawny in body or mind," all of which are unwomanly; a womanly woman is gentle and beautiful, and work damages both of those qualities.

## Worksheet 7: Presidential Elections (page 16)

You could have students write their answers to the questions, or you could lead students in a class discussion of responses to the questions.

1. **1912**—Wilson, 42% popular, 82% electoral; Roosevelt, 28% popular, 17% electoral; Taft, 23% popular, 1% electoral; Debs, 6% popular, 0% electoral; Chafin, 1% popular, 0% electoral.

**1916**—Wilson, 50% popular, 52% electoral; Hughes, 46% popular, 48% electoral; Benson, 3% popular, 0% electoral; Hanly, 1% popular, 0% electoral.

2. **1912**—Taft won Vermont and Utah; Roosevelt took Washington, California, South Dakota, Minnesota, Michigan, and Pennsylvania; Wilson took the rest.

    **1916**—Hughes won Oregon, South Dakota, Minnesota, Wisconsin, Iowa, Indiana, Illinois, Michigan, West Virginia, Pennsylvania, Delaware, New Jersey, New York, Connecticut, Rhode Island, Massachusetts, Vermont, and Maine. Wilson won the rest.

3. Popular vs. electoral vote percentages are quite different for each of the three major candidates in 1912, but they are similar for the two major candidates in 1916. Most voters in 1912 voted for reform candidates—Wilson and Roosevelt, plus Debs. Wilson won by a much smaller margin (in popular and electoral votes) in 1916, because the Republicans weren't split as they had been in 1912.

4. In 1916 Wilson lost some states he had won in 1912—Oregon, Iowa, Wisconsin, Indiana, Illinois, West Virginia, Delaware, New Jersey, New York, Connecticut, Rhode Island, Massachusetts, and Maine. He won Washington and California, which he had lost in 1912.

## Worksheet 8: TR Talks (page 17)

You could ask for volunteers to respond to each quote. You could divide the class into teams and make the activity into a team competition. Or you could assign the activity as written homework or written classwork, team or individual.

"Men with the muck-rake . . ."—refers to Progressive journalists and the articles they wrote exposing political corruption and political, social, and economic abuses.

"The *Maine* . . ."—the blowing up of the U.S. ship *Maine* in Havana harbor, which triggered the Spanish-American War of 1898; TR was speaking as assistant secretary of the Navy.

"I hate the man . . ."—a statement of TR's strong feelings about conservation and wilderness preservation.

"a square deal"—TR's 1904 campaign slogan; he wanted business and government to treat the American people fairly.

"Don't bluster. . . ."—applies to TR's approach to foreign policy.

"The White House . . ."—TR's opinion that being president of the U.S. is an excellent opportunity to promote his ideas about what is best for the country.

"It's a dreadful thing . . ."—refers to TR becoming president because of McKinley's assassination in 1901.

"malefactors of great wealth"—TR's description of the leaders of big business and trusts.

". . . gorged boa constrictor . . ."—comment about speculation that the U.S. might intend to annex the Dominican Republic.

"The Vice Presidency . . ."—TR's comment on becoming the Republicans' candidate for vice president on the McKinley ticket of 1900.

". . . bull moose"—comment TR made when the new Progressive party made him its presidential candidate in 1912; gave the party its nickname, the Bull Moose party.

"Speak softly . . ."—TR's favorite saying; refers to foreign policy of not speaking aggressively and making threats, but making it clear that U.S. military power will be used to enforce U.S. foreign policy objectives.

". . . Colombian rulers . . ."—refers to attempts to get an agreement with Colombia to build a canal in the Colombian province of Panama.

## Worksheet 9: National Lands (page 18)

National Parks: Yellowstone, northwest WY (some MT, ID); Sequoia, central CA; Yosemite, east-central CA; Grand Canyon, northwest AZ; Mount Ranier, southwest WA; Crater Lake, south OR; Wind Cave, southwest SD; Petrified Forest, northeast AZ; Mesa Verde, southwest CO; Lassen Volcanic, north-central CA; Olympic, northwest WA; Glacier, northwest MT.

National Monuments: Devil's Tower, northeast WY (the first national monument); Chaco Canyon, northwest NM; Pinnacles, west-central CA; Muir

Woods, northern CA; Natural Bridges, southeast UT.

Wildlife Preserves: Pelican Island, FL; Wichita Game Preserves, KS; National Bison Range, western MT; Klamath and Malheur Reserves, OR.

For maps of national lands on the Internet, see "Mapping the National Parks" at http://memory. loc.gov/ammem/gmdhtml/nphtml/nphome.html.

## Worksheet 10: Progressive Era Time Line (page 19)

1890  NAWSA is founded

1898  Initiative and referendum system adopted in South Dakota

1900  Robert La Follette elected governor of Wisconsin
Eugene Debs runs for president on Socialist ticket
Direct primaries held in Minnesota

1901  Theodore Roosevelt becomes president

1902  Tarbell and Steffens articles appear in *McClure's*
National coal strike
Initiative system adopted in Oregon
Dead Indian Land Act, Reclamation Act

1903  W. E. B. DuBois's *The Souls of Black Folk* is published
Elkins Railroad Act
Direct primary enacted in Wisconsin
Department of Commerce and Labor is established

1904  Northern Securities case
National Child Labor Committee is established
Theodore Roosevelt is elected

1905  IWW is founded
*Lochner* v. *New York*

1906  Upton Sinclair's *The Jungle* is published
Meat Inspection Act, Pure Food and Drug Act, Hepburn Act

1907  Panic of 1907

1908  Taft is elected president
*Muller* v. *Oregon*

1909  NAACP is founded

1910  Mann Act
Ballinger-Pinchot affair

1912  Children's Bureau for Department of Labor is established
Woodrow Wilson is elected president, Roosevelt runs as Progressive candidate

1913  Sixteenth and Seventeenth Amendments ratified
Underwood Tariff Act, Federal Reserve Act

1914  Congressional Union is established
Federal Trade Commission Act, Clayton Antitrust Act

1916  Keating-Owen Child Labor Act

1919  Eighteenth Amendment ratified

1920  Nineteenth Amendment ratified

## Additional Activity Suggestions

You could have students do any of the following activities.

1. Investigate something in your school, neighborhood, or city/town that you think needs changing, and then write a muckraking article about it.

2. Write a formal proposal for the reform of election campaign financing and fund-raising. Explain why your proposal would be an effective remedy for the failings of the current system. Also explain how you would build support for your proposal.

3. Create state-by-state maps of the results of some recent presidential elections. What do the maps show about regional voting trends?

4. Visit a national park, national wildlife refuge, national monument, or national forest in your area. Take photos, collect trail guides and visitor information, and create a classroom display about the attractions and value of this piece of national land. Or take a virtual tour of national land on-line at the National Park Service web site at http://www.nps.gov/.

5. Role-play a debate in Congress about approval of one of the Progressive amendments to the U.S. Constitution.

6. Write a biography of one of the Progressive-era reformers, such as Jacob Riis, Lincoln Steffens, Robert La Follette, Ida Tarbell, Jane Addams, Margaret Sanger, or Mary Church Terrell.

7. Learn to do some of the popular "animal" dances of the early 1900s, like the camel walk, buzzard lope, bunny hop, grizzly bear, turkey trot, chicken scratch, and kangaroo dip.

8. Investigate any of these Internet sites:
   "The Evolution of the Conservation Movement 1850–1920":
   http://memory.loc.gov/ammem/amrvhtml/conshome.html
   "The Last Days of a President: Films of McKinley and the Pan-American Exposition, 1901":
   http://memory.loc.gov/ammem/papr/mckhome.html
   "Theodore Roosevelt: His Life and Times on Film":
   http://memory.loc.gov/ammem/trfhtml/trfhome.html

### Assessment

1. Create a chart of significant Progressive reforms at the local, state, and national levels.

2. List Progressive-era reform issues, then social reform issues of today. Compare these issues. How are they different? How are they similar? Do some reforms that Progressives targeted remain to be made today?

## Unit 2: The United States and World Affairs

### Worksheet 1: The United States in Latin America (page 27)

**Cuba**—1898–1902, 1906–09, 1912, U.S. troop occupation

**Dominican Republic**—1904–05, 1916–24, U.S. troops, customs takeover

**Guatemala**—1920, U.S. troops

**Haiti**—1915–34, U.S. troops, financial takeover

**Honduras**—1919, U.S. troops

**Mexico**—1914, 1916–17, U.S. troops

**Nicaragua**—1910–33, U.S. troops, customs takeover

**Panama**—1903, U.S. warships allow revolution, U.S. creates Canal Zone

**Puerto Rico**—1898–1900, U.S. troops; inhabitants granted U.S. citizenship, 1917

**Virgin Islands**—1917, purchased from Denmark by U.S.

### Worksheet 2: U.S. Policy and Latin America (page 30)

You could have students discuss the answers to the questions in class (in small groups or as a whole-class discussion), or they could write their answers to the questions as a homework assignment.

1. The U.S. will intervene in the domestic affairs of Latin American countries whenever the U.S. thinks conditions in a given nation threaten U.S. economic or security interests.

2. The U.S. will control Latin American countries through financial means rather than through the use of U.S. military forces. (In practice, U.S. troops as well as dollars were used.)

3. a. The object of U.S. foreign policy is to support and promote the development of democratic governments.

   b. Wilson disapproved of the way in which Huerta took power and so supported Huerta's rival, Carranza.

   c. He continued the U.S. military presence in Nicaragua and sent troops into Haiti and the Dominican Republic.

4. Stimson and Hoover started the "good neighbor" policy, recognizing the rights of Latin American nations to conduct their internal policies as they saw fit.

5. Roosevelt's policy was similar to the Stimson/Hoover policy.

### Worksheet 6: Enter the War: Yes or No? (page 34)

1. To strike back against German submarine warfare and to make the world "safe for democracy."

2. Because Great Britain also has set up war zones, with mines that sink ships without warning. If Germany is guilty, so is Great Britain.

3. Fighting in the war would not be a benefit to humanity. It would benefit only munition manufacturers, stockbrokers, and bond dealers.

4. The United States should treat both Britain and Germany in the same way and refuse to trade with either of them until they end their war zones on the seas—that will end the attacks on U.S. ships.

## Worksheet 7:
## Weapons of the War (page 35)

1. machine gun; its rapid, continuous fire can kill and wound many men in a short time.

2. tank; it can advance on enemy soldiers and fire on them, with soldiers inside the tank protected from enemy fire.

3. submarine (U-boat); it attacks ships with underwater torpedoes, can approach enemy ships underwater unseen, and strike without warning.

4. airplane; first use of the airplane in war—it bombs and shoots troops, cities, and civilians, causing great damage to all.

5. gas mask; it protects against poison gas, which blinds enemy soldiers, destroys their lungs, and/or damages their skin, blood, and/or nervous systems.

## Worksheet 8:
## Life in the Trenches (page 36)

Interested students could read more or all of Empey's *Over the Top*. It's a lively and vivid account of the experiences of trench warfare and life. Another account, of a French soldier's experiences, is Henri Barbusse's *Under Fire*.

## Worksheet 9: War Propaganda (pages 37–38)

"Beat Back the Hun"—War aim: to demonize the enemy, raise money through sale of liberty bonds; Appeal, symbol, slogan: visual depiction of enemy as evil, destroying thug; disparaging word ("The Hun") for the enemy; appeal to patriotism to buy war bonds with the slogan "Liberty Bonds."

"Blood or Bread"—War aim: conserve resources so more is available to support the armed forces;

Appeal, symbol, slogan: visual appeal of the strong, valiant soldier and the wounded soldier who may have given his life for his country; slogan "Blood or Bread"; appeal to patriotism in sacrificing for your country.

"I Want You for U.S. Army"—War aim: to encourage the enlistment of able-bodied men to fight in the war; Appeal, symbol, slogan: visual appeal of patriotic father figure (Uncle Sam) using implied flattery via the slogan "I Want You" to appeal to the individual and suggest that *he* is the person the Army needs.

"What Are You Doing to Help?"—War aim: support the Red Cross, which helps soldiers; Appeal, symbol, slogan: visual appeal of the valiant wounded soldier and the compassionate female caregiver; woman as nurturer, caregiver, mother figure; appeal to support the Red Cross with membership fees.

## Worksheet 11:
## Your Right to Free Speech (page 40)

People were arrested for each of these actions, as violations of the Espionage and Sedition Acts of 1917 and 1918.

### Additional Activity Suggestions

You could have the students do any of the following activities.

1. Research and report on a specific case of U.S. interference in the internal affairs of a Latin American country in the years from 1900 to 1930. Note which type of U.S. foreign policy toward Latin America was exercised in this incident.

2. Read the Monroe Doctrine, as stated by U.S. President Monroe in 1823. (You can find this in book 4 of this series, *Focus on U.S. History: The Era of Expansion and Reform.*) Compare the Monroe Doctrine with the Roosevelt Corollary. Is the Corollary a legitimate extension or a distortion of the Doctrine?

3. Did the Espionage and Sedition Acts violate the First Amendment right to free speech? For the Supreme Court's opinion, see *Schenck* v. *U.S.* and *Abrams* v. *U.S.* (both 1919). Write your own decision about this question, framed in the style of a court ruling. You can access *Schenck* and *Abrams* on the Internet at

"Historic Supreme Court Decisions," http://supct.law.cornell.edu/supct/cases/name.htm.

4. Create a model or engineering drawing of the construction of the Panama Canal. Or, imagine you are a worker on the canal project, and write a series of letters or diary entries describing your experiences.

5. Evaluate U.S. foreign policy toward Asia. What outlook toward Asia and Asians do the Open Door notes of John Hay and the Gentlemen's Agreement of 1907–08 express?

6. Create a classroom display of cartoons about Theodore Roosevelt's foreign policy in Latin America.

7. Describe U.S. policy toward Mexico under President Wilson from the point of view of a Mexican citizen or a Mexican-American. Keep in mind the remark of Mexico's ruler, Porfirio Díaz, "Poor Mexico. So far from God and close to the United States."

8. Create a map showing the activities of the American Expeditionary Force in Europe during World War I. You could use this map and photographs of World War I battle scenes to create a bulletin board display about the war.

9. Present a show of World War I songs, like "Over There" and "I Didn't Raise My Boy to Be a Soldier."

10. Investigate any of these Internet sites:
    "American Leaders Speak: Recordings from World War I and the 1920 Election":
    http://memory.loc.gov/ammem/nforSpeakers01.html
    "American Posters of World War I":
    http://www.library.georgetown.edu/dept/speccoll/amposter.html
    "My Mother's War: Mementos of World War I":
    http://www.geocities.com/Athens/Acropolis/4144/mom/momentry.html
    "Photos of the Great War: World War I Image Archive":
    http://www.ukans.edu/~kansite/ww_one/photos/greatwar.htm
    "World War I: Trenches on the Web (An Internet History of the Great War)":

http://worldwar1.com
"World War I Cartoons":
http://rutland.k12.vt.us/jpeterso/uboatcar.htm

### Assessment

1. Analyze the extent to which Woodrow Wilson's Fourteen Points were and were not incorporated into the treaties ending World War I.

2. Summarize U.S. actions in Latin America between 1900 and 1930. (The completed Worksheet 1, including the Extra Challenge, would satisfy this assessment requirement.)

3. Discuss the issue of whether or not the United States really needed to declare war on Germany and enter World War I.

## *Unit 3. The Roaring Twenties*

### Worksheet 1: The Urban-Rural Change (page 49)

1. More people lived in urban areas than in rural areas for the first time. Yes, it continued.

2. rural—46,000; urban—30,000

3. rural—54,000; urban—69,000

4. Urban population increased much more rapidly than rural population did. People were moving to cities for jobs, excitement of urban life; African-Americans and immigrants especially came to cities for economic opportunities.

### Worksheet 3: Returning African-American Soldiers (page 51)

1. Lynching—two blacks per week lynched for the past fifty years. Disfranchisement—robs blacks of their only protection against whites and the poor of their only protection against the rich. Encouraging ignorance—a "dominant minority" wants to prevent blacks from being educated and then declares that uneducated blacks are incapable of being educated. Stealing—whites cheat blacks out of their land, their labor, and their savings; whites reduce wages, raise rents, tax blacks without

representation; they keep blacks poor and dependent on charity and then criticize blacks for being poor. Insulting—a continuous campaign of defaming black people and, through segregation, branding them as inferior in all spheres of life; also, treatment of any black complaints about this as "unwarranted assumption and treason."

## Worksheet 4: African-American Life in the North (page 52)

Suggest that students read the entire short story by Dorothy West. One anthology that includes the story is *The Portable Harlem Renaissance Reader,* Viking Penguin, 1994.

## Worksheet 6: Reading the Immigration Graph (page 54)

1. 1913; 1,200,000

2. from 1913 to 1919; World War I, fought from 1914 to 1917, slowed immigration down to a trickle

3. 1921; 805,000

4. It dropped from a high of 805,000 in 1921 to below 300,000 in 1929 because restrictive immigration laws were passed in 1921 (the Johnson Act/Emergency Quota Act) and 1924 (the National Origins Act).

5. It dropped to as low as 23,000 in 1933 because the Great Depression happened in the 1930s and people no longer had the money to immigrate, nor the reason to, since jobs were no longer available to immigrants in the United States.

6. about 1,177,000

## Worksheet 7: The "New Woman" (page 55)

1. The right to vote: gave women political equality with men—their opinions and support now counted with politicians (at least to some degree)

2. 1920s flapper: she rejected constricting clothing and constricting social conventions

3. Washing machine: this and other labor-saving household devices freed women (supposedly) from some of the drudgery of household chores

## Worksheet 8: Women and Work, 1920s Style (page 56)

Students can answer the activity's questions in an essay or in a class/small group discussion.

## Worksheet 10: Twenties Talk (page 58)

| | |
|---|---|
| **flapper:** thoroughly modern young woman | **giggle water:** alcoholic drink |
| **jellybean:** boyfriend of a flapper | **ossified:** drunk |
| **It:** sex appeal | **gams:** a girl's legs |
| **sheik:** 1920s-style man with sex appeal | **whoopee:** boisterous, happy fun |
| **sheba:** 1920s-style woman with sex appeal | **park:** kiss in a car |
| **snugglepup:** young man who often pets | **copacetic:** excellent |
| **flat tire:** person who's a big bore | **banana oil:** not true! |
| **two-timer:** boy/girlfriend who cheats | **horsefeathers:** nonsense |
| **big cheese:** important person | **carry a torch:** yearn for a lost love |
| **goof:** a strange person | **bee's knees:** anything terrific |
| **lounge lizard:** ladies' man | **jake:** okay |
| **the cat's meow:** anything terrific | **spiffy:** excellent, top-notch |
| **double date:** two couples on a date together | **neck:** kiss for an extended period |
| **cheaters:** eyeglasses | **dogs:** human feet |

Challenge students to carry on a 1920s conversation with lots of twenties slang.

## Worksheet 11: Sports Stars (page 59)

Babe Ruth, a; Red Grange, c; Bill Tilden, g; Man o' War, e; Gertrude Ederle, f; Knute Rockne, c; Jim Thorpe, h, c; Helen Wills, g; Bobby Jones, d; Johnny Weissmuller, f; Jack Dempsey, b

## Worksheet 12: The Automobile and the American Landscape (page 60)

Advertisers quickly developed a new form of getting across their messages to motorists: the billboard. The landscape became littered with these large advertising signs.

Gas stations sprouted up everywhere to provide fuel for cars.

Roadside quick-food restaurants catered to people out for a ride.

Tourist courts were the 1930s precursors of the motel; roadside rows and semicircles of small cabins were something new, offering more comfortable alternatives to camping out for the legions of motorists who vacationed with their cars.

The car created a new type of town—the suburb, single-family homes outside of the city, made possible because people could live in one place and drive to their jobs in another place; housewives could drive to shopping centers. Suburban sprawl was beginning.

For early motoring information on the Internet, see:
"Petersen Automotive Museum: Vintage Automobile Tourism Slide Show":
http://www.petersen.org/online/indexa.htm
"Roadside America":
http://www.roadsideamerica.com

### Additional Activity Suggestions

You could have the students do any of the following activities.

1. Take part in a class choral reading of the famous baseball poem "Casey at the Bat."

2. Conduct your own investigation into the Sacco-Vanzetti case. Then make a persuasive argument for the guilt or innocence of both men, or just one of them.

3. Create an illustrated report on the spread of the Ku Klux Klan during the 1920s. Explain the Klan's attitude toward various minority groups and why Klan membership grew so large during these years.

4. Use selections from the Scopes trial or from the drama *Inherit the Wind* to illustrate how the views of William Jennings Bryan and Clarence Darrow differed. Relate the arguments of Bryan and Darrow to the revival in recent times of the creationist *vs.* evolutionary issue and teaching content in public schools.

5. Create a classroom display of photographs of your town or city in the 1920s. You could add contrasting photos of these same scenes today.

6. Compare media and recreation that brought Americans information and entertainment in the 1920s with media and recreation today.

7. Write an in-depth report on one of the figures of the Harlem Renaissance. Be sure to discuss the ideas and issues this person portrayed in her or his work.

8. Create a classroom display of the work of artists of the Ashcan school.

9. Enjoy a fad of the 1920s. Play a game of mah-jongg. Dance the Charleston.

10. Investigate any of these Internet sites:
"By Popular Demand: Jackie Robinson and Other Baseball Highlights 1860s–1960s":
http://memory.loc.gov/ammem/jrhtm/jrhome.html
"Flapper Culture and Style":
http://www.pandorasbox.com/flapper.html
"Universal Black Pages":
http://www.ubp.com/

### Assessment

1. Explain why Al Smith lost the 1928 election, and describe a Democratic (or other) candidate who might have had any chance of beating Herbert Hoover in 1928.

2. Use illustrations from a 1920s Sears or Montgomery Ward catalog to show new inventions

and technological advances that affected the lives of Americans in the 1920s.

# Unit 4: The Great Depression

## Worksheet 2: Presidential Elections: 1928 and 1932 (page 67)

1. States in the Deep South were traditional Democratic strongholds; in other areas, even Democrats wouldn't support Smith's Catholicism, urban background, anti-Prohibition stand, and political machine ties.

2. The country had enjoyed a long period of prosperity under Republican presidents, and most people were not interested in change.

3. By 1932, the country was in the depths of the Depression, and Hoover had done little to help people hard hit by it.

4. Democrats were beginning to draw together a new coalition based not on regions but on class: immigrants, farmers, industrial laborers, ethnic/religious minorities, city people, and the rural poor.

Answers for the Extra Challenge: (5) Taft lost a lot of support, but his party was split in 1912. (6) Their vote count increased—except for FDR's third and fourth run, when his vote totals went down somewhat. (7) If a president's popularity with voters increases, he'll be reelected. If his popularity decreases at all, he'll lose.

## Worksheet 3: Your Stock Market Losses (page 68)

Show students how to figure the total cost of 100 shares of stock by converting the fractions in the stock prices to decimals: $1/8 = .125$; $3/8 = .375$; $5/8 = .625$; $7/8 = .875$. Also, explain to students how a small investor could have such a large portfolio—by buying on margin, using profits from earlier stock transactions.

|  | 9/3/29 | 10/29/29 |
|---|---|---|
| Auburn Auto | $ 49,800.00 | $ 12,000 |
| Electric Auto-Lite | 15,400.00 | 5,000 |
| Brooklyn Union Gas | 24,700.00 | 10,000 |
| Purity Bakeries | 14,437.50 | 5,500 |
| Montgomery Ward | 13,787.50 | 4,950 |
| Radio Corporation | 10,100.00 | 2,600 |
| White Sewing Machine | 1,787.50 | 100 |
| Total | $ 130,012.50 | $ 40,150 |

Loss: $89,862.50

Total cost of the stock purchases on 9/3/29: $130,012.50

Balance that you owe to your broker (50%): $ 65,006.25

Current value of the stocks: $ 40,150.00

The current value of the stocks is less than the amount you owe your broker. You are wiped out.

## Worksheet 4: Hooverisms (page 69)

1. a wild rabbit caught by a country person for food

2. empty pocket turned inside out

3. old newspaper wrapped around a homeless person for warmth while sleeping

4. a car with the front (engine) end cut off and pulled by a mule or horse

5. a sack containing all of a homeless person's belongings

6. shoes with holes in the soles plugged up with newspaper or cardboard

7. a shantytown full of shelters made of cast-off materials, such as tin, burlap, and cardboard, home to homeless, unemployed people

## Answers for the Extra Challenge: (69)

Hoover had saved millions of Belgians from starvation during World War I as head of the Belgian Relief Commission. To "hoover" in Finnish meant to help.

## Worksheet 7:
## The Great Depression at Home (page 73)

This would be a good group activity and could serve as an assessment vehicle.

## Worksheet 8: Women of the Thirties: In Real Life (page 74)

<u>Eleanor Roosevelt:</u> First Lady, social activist, advocate for civil rights.

<u>Frances Perkins:</u> FDR's secretary of labor; first female Cabinet member; outspoken.

<u>Mary McLeod Bethune:</u> Leading member of FDR's Black Cabinet that advised him on racial matters; member of National Youth Administration; daughter of ex-slaves.

<u>Babe Didrickson Zaharias:</u> phenomenal sports star; won gold medals at the 1932 Olympics in track and field (javelin throw and high hurdles); became a champion golfer; excellent at all sports.

<u>Bonnie Parker:</u> with partner Clyde Barrow, went on a bank- and store-robbing crime spree in the Southwest; killed in an ambush by law enforcement officials.

## Worksheet 9: Women of the Thirties: On the Screen (page 75)

<u>Scarlett O'Hara:</u> fictional heroine of the Civil War epic *Gone with the Wind;* played in Oscar-winning performance by Vivien Leigh; she survives the destruction of her world with her spirit unbroken— an inspiration for Depression-era viewers whose world was crumbling around them.

<u>Shirley Temple:</u> America's adorable child star, made 27 films in the 1930s; her cheery, bubbly personality lifted Americans' spirits.

<u>Snow White:</u> the heroine of Disney's first feature-length cartoon film; she allowed Depression-era audiences to escape into a long-ago fairy-tale world, where everything turns out well in the end.

<u>Ginger Rogers:</u> brought grace and elegance to Depression audiences as she twirled across the screen with dance partner Fred Astaire.

## Additional Activity Suggestions

You could have the students do any of the following activities.

1. Listen to the *War of the Worlds* radio broadcast. You might find a tape of it at your local library. Or try the Internet site "The 1938 'War of the Worlds' Radio Broadcast Waves" at http://earthstation1.simplenet.com/wotw.html.

2. Create a classroom display of Depression-era photographs taken by photographers working for the Farm Security Administration and the WPA. You could add photos of the Roaring Twenties to show how life for Americans changed in the thirties.

3. Explain scientifically how the Dust Bowl developed and how changed farming practices on the Great Plains have prevented another Dust Bowl from occurring.

4. Read the books by Mildred Taylor about the Logans, a close-knit African-American farm family in the rural South of the 1930s, including *Roll of Thunder, Hear My Cry,* and *Let the Circle Be Unbroken.*

5. Read the John Steinbeck classic, *The Grapes of Wrath*, to become part of the experience of Dust Bowl refugees who struggle to make a new life in California.

6. Play recordings of (or get the sheet music for) Depression-era songs, such as "Brother, Can You Spare a Dime?" "Life Is Just a Bowl of Cherries," and "A Shanty in Old Shantytown." How do the lyrics of these songs reflect the economic difficulties of the times?

7. Investigate any of these Internet sites:
   "The Access Indiana Teaching and Learning Center: The Great Depression": http://tlc.ai.org/depressi.htm
   "The African-American Mosaic: A Library of Congress Resource Guide for the Study of Black History and Culture": http://lcweb.loc.gov/exhibits/african/intro.html
   "America from the Great Depression to World War II: Photographs from the FSA-OWI, 1935–1945": http://memory.loc.gov/ammem/fsowhome.html

"American Life Histories: Manuscripts from the Federal Writers' Project, 1936–1940": http://memory.loc.gov/ammem/wpaintr/wpahome.html

"Surviving the Dust Bowl (The American Experience)": http://www.pbs.org/wgbh/amex/dustbowl/

### Assessment

1. Create an in-depth report on Eleanor Roosevelt, Frances Perkins, or Mary McLeod Bethune describing how this woman affected and was also a product of her times.

2. A thoughtfully completed Worksheet 1, Your Economic Problems, will demonstrate a knowledge of the causes of the Great Depression.

3. Worksheets 5 and 7 would serve as effective assessment vehicles to demonstrate students' understanding of the impact of the Great Depression on Americans.

## *Unit 5. The New Deal*

### Worksheet 2: Presidential Campaigns, 1900–1932 (page 85)

| | | | |
|---|---|---|---|
| 1. a | 4. j | 7. f | 10. h |
| 2. b | 5. g | 8. c | |
| 3. e | 6. d | 9. i | |

### Worksheet 3: TR and FDR (page 86)

| | Theodore Roosevelt | Franklin D. Roosevelt |
|---|---|---|
| **family background** | rich, indulged | rich, indulged |
| **health/illness** | sickly, asthmatic as a child; worked hard to make himself a robust adult | stricken with polio as an adult, came back with vigor although paralyzed from the waist down |
| **college he graduated from** | Harvard University | Harvard University |
| **first elected state office** | New York state legislature | New York state legislature |
| **highest elected state office** | governor of New York | governor of New York |
| **high-level appointive federal office in Washington, DC** | assistant secretary of the U.S. Navy | assistant secretary of the U.S. navy |
| **first national office campaigned for (and the outcome)** | vice president of the U.S. (won) | vice president of the U.S. (lost) |
| **political party** | Republican | Democratic |
| **political philosophy** | progressive | progressive |
| **attitude toward being president of the U.S.** | "dee-lighted" to be president; "I don't think any family has enjoyed the White House more than we have." | "Wouldn't you be president if you could? Wouldn't anybody?" |

## Worksheet 5:
## You and the New Deal (page 90)

Answers will vary. Here are some possibilities.

1. Agricultural Adjustment Administration (AAA), Rural Electrification Administration (REA), Soil Conservation Program, Farm Credit Administration, Farm Security Administration, Resettlement Administration, Commodity Credit Corporation.

2. Home Owners Loan Corp. (HOLC); your later bank deposits would be insured through the Federal Deposit Insurance Corp. (FDIC).

3. Civilian Conservation Corps (CCC), National Youth Administration (NYA); also, Works Progress Administration (WPA) and Public Works Administration (PWA).

4. National Labor Relations Board (NLRB), Wagner Act, Fair Labor Standards Act.

5. You're out of luck now, but your future stock market transactions will benefit from the Federal Securities Act and the Securities & Exchange Commission (SEC).

6. Works Progress Administration (WPA).

7. Social Security Administration.

## Worksheet 8: No New Deal! (page 93)

Sinclair's plan: government takeover of closed factories and unused land for productive use by the unemployed. Real problem: closed factories and unproductive land and people out of work as a result. Supporters: more radical people, left-wingers.

Coughlin's plan: government takeover of banks, expanded money supply with silver (not gold) standard, suppression of unions. Real problem: inadequacies in the money supply. Supporters: Catholics, working class and urban lower-middle class, anti-Semites.

Townsend's plan: Old-Age Revolving Pensions—every person over 60 years old who had no job would receive $200 a month from the federal government; recipients had to spend the money within 30 days. A 2% tax on commercial transactions would pay for the program. Creates jobs for the unemployed via openings when people aged 60 and older retire; pension spending would increase consumer spending and thus boost production, which would create more

jobs. Real problem: plight of elderly Americans, with no pensions, no jobs, and no medical insurance. Supporters: older Americans.

## Worksheet 9: The Supreme Court and the New Deal (page 94)

You can find more complete excerpts from these two decisions in *The Annals of America,* Vol. 14, and *Documents of American History,* Vol. 2 (see Resources section). You can also access *Adkins* and *West Coast* on the Internet at "Historic Supreme Court Decisions," http://supct.law.cornell.edu/supct/cases/name. htm.

## Worksheet 10: FDR and the Supreme Court (page 95)

1. Section 1 of Article III simply provides for "one supreme Court" with an unspecified number of judges, who "shall hold their offices during good behaviour" and shall receive a salary that cannot be lowered during their term on the Court.

2. The Court had (and still has) nine justices when Roosevelt was president. His plan would add one new justice to the Court for each existing justice over the age of 70 who chose not to retire, up to a total of six additional justices.

3. Congress was very opposed to the plan, as were most newspaper editors and lawyers. Public opinion was fairly evenly divided, but those opposed to the plan were very vocal. Americans strongly supported the independence of the judiciary from political pressures and were not pleased at the prospect of Roosevelt attempting to manipulate the Court's decisions. Many people feared that if Roosevelt could manipulate the Court into favoring his New Deal proposals, later presidents and politicians could do the same thing, bending the Court's opinions either to the right or to the left in the interests of a particular political point of view.

## Worksheet 11:
## The New Deal Time Line (page 96)

The items from the What Is It? New Deal game have been added to this time line.

1929  Crash of N.Y. stock market

1932  Bonus Army march

1932  Franklin Roosevelt elected president

1933  Roosevelt inaugurated
      Nationwide bank holiday
      Hundred Days
      Federal Emergency Relief Administration
        (FERA)
      Civilian Conservation Corps (CCC)
      Federal Deposit Insurance Corp. (FDIC)
      Home Owners Loan Corp. (HOLC)
      Federal Securities Act
      Public Works Administration (PWA)
      National Recovery Administration (NRA)
      Agricultural Adjustment Administration
        (AAA)
      Tennessee Valley Authority (TVA)
      Farm Credit Administration
      Commodity Credit Corporation
      Repeal of Eighteenth Amendment
      Dust Bowl storms begin

1934  American Liberty League founded
      Townsend Clubs sprout
      Indian Reorganization Act
      Father Coughlin creates National Union for
        Social Justice
      Huey Long creates Share Our Wealth Society
      Securities & Exchange Commission (SEC)
      Federal Housing Administration (FHA)

1935  Harlem race riot
      *Schechter Poultry Corp.* v. *U.S.*
      Second Hundred Days
      National Labor Relations Board (NLRB)
      Works Progress Administration (WPA)
      Rural Electrification Administration (REA)
      National Youth Administration (NYA)
      Social Security Administration
      Resettlement Administration
      Revenue Act (Wealth Tax Act)
      Public Utilities Holding Company Act
      Banking Act
      Long assassinated

1936  Boulder Dam built
      Soil Conservation Program
      *Moorhead* v. *Tipaldo*
      Roosevelt reelected
      *Butler* v. *U.S.*
      CIO formed

1937  Sit-down strikes
      Farm Security Administration
      *N.L.R.B.* v. *Jones & Laughlin Steel Corp.*
      Roosevelt court-packing plan

1937–38  Roosevelt recession

1938  Fair Labor Standards Act

1939  Marian Anderson sings at the Lincoln
        Memorial
      World War II begins in Europe

## Additional Activity Suggestions

You could have students do any of the following activities.

1.  Graph unemployment in the United States from 1929 through 1940.

2.  Create a diagram or a model of a multipurpose New Deal dam and river control system, like the Boulder Dam or a portion of the Tennessee Valley Authority project.

3.  Research and report on Roosevelt's "Black Cabinet" and its individual members.

4.  Explain the effects of the Depression and the New Deal on the U.S. labor movement through the lyrics of 1930s union songs, such as "Joe Hill," "Union Maid," "Which Side Are You On?" and "Brother, Can You Spare a Dime?"

5.  Make a chart that summarizes Supreme Court decisions on Progressive and New Deal legislation.

6.  Trace the evolution of federal policy and white society's attitudes toward Native Americans from the Dawes Act of 1887 through the New Deal.

7.  Investigate any of these Internet sites:
    "America from the Great Depression to World War II: Photographs from the FSA-OWI, 1935–1945":
    http://memory.loc.gov/ammem/fsowhome.html
    "American Life Histories: Manuscripts from the Federal Writers' Project, 1936–1940":
    http://memory.loc.gov/ammem/wpaintr/wpahome.html
    "FDR Cartoon Archive":
    http://www.nisk.k12.ny.us/fdr/

"A New Deal for the Arts":
   http://www.nara.gov/exhall/newdeal/
   newdeal.html
"A New Deal Network":
   http://newdeal.feri.org/

## Assessment

1. Compare Herbert Hoover's and Franklin D. Roosevelt's policies for addressing the problems of the Great Depression. Why were Hoover's policies less effective than Roosevelt's?

2. A thoughtfully completed Worksheet 6 would effectively demonstrate students' knowledge of the ways in which various New Deal programs could help different Americans.

# ADDITIONAL RESOURCES

## Historical Fiction for Students

Aaron, Chester. *Lackawana* (Great Depression)

Armstrong, William. *Sounder* (rural black family in the South, early 1900s)

Avi. *Shadrach's Crossing* (smuggling during Prohibition)

Bess, Clayton. *Tracks* (Great Depression)

Bolton, Carol. *Never Jam Today* (women's suffrage)

Constant, Alberta Wilson. *Does Anyone Care About Lou Emma Miller?* (women's suffrage)

Curtis, Christopher Paul. *Bud, Not Buddy* (Great Depression)

De Felice, Cynthia. *Nowhere to Call Home* (riding the rails, Great Depression)

Edwards, Pat. *Nelda* (migrant worker family in 1930s)

Fitzgerald, F. Scott. *The Great Gatsby* (the Jazz Age, the 1920s)

Hamilton, Liz. *I Remember Valentine* (Great Depression)

Hesse, Karen. *Out of the Dust* (Dust Bowl Oklahoma)

Hunt, Irene. *No Promises in the Wind* (Great Depression)

Lawrence, Jerome, and Robert E. Lee, *Inherit the Wind* (drama about the Scopes trial)

Lee, Harper. *To Kill a Mockingbird* (black/white tensions in southern town, 1930s)

Perez, N.A. *Breaker* (boy mine worker, early 1900s)

*The Portable Harlem Renaissance Reader*, Viking Penguin

Remarque, Erich Maria. *All Quiet on the Western Front* (World War I)

Sinclair, Upton. *The Jungle* (immigrants in Chicago, c. 1900)

Steinbeck, John. *The Grapes of Wrath* (Dust Bowl refugees' trek to California)

Taylor, Mildred. *Roll of Thunder, Hear My Cry,* and *Let the Circle Be Unbroken* (African-American farmers in rural South, 1930s)

Thrasher, Crystal. *A Taste of Daylight* (and four other titles in the series; Great Depression)

Trumbo, Dalton. *Johnny Got His Gun* (World War I)

Yep, Lawrence. *Dragonwings* (Chinese immigrants in San Francisco, early 1900s)

Zeier, Joan. *Elderberry Thicket* (Great Depression)

## Nonfiction for Students

Agee, James, and Walker Evans. *You Have Seen Their Faces* and *Let Us Now Praise Famous Men*

Allen, Frederick. *Only Yesterday* (1920s) and *Since Yesterday* (1930s)

Banks, Ann. *First-Person America*

Barbusse, Henri. *Under Fire*

Cooper, Michael L. *Bound for the Promised Land: The Great Black Migration*

DuBois, W. E. B. *Writings*

Empey, Guy. *Over the Top*

Freedman, Russell. *Babe Didrikson Zaharias* and *Kids at Work: Lewis Hine and the Crusade Against Child Labor*

Jennings, Peter, and Todd Brewster. *The Century for Young People*

Katz, William Loren. *An Album of the Great Depression*

Lemann, Nicholas. *The Promised Land: The Great Black Migration and How It Changed America*

Meltzer, Milton. *The Black Americans: A History in Their Own Words*

Meltzer, Milton. *Brother, Can You Spare a Dime?*

Reader's Digest. *Our Glorious Century*

Riis, Jacob. *How the Other Half Lives*

*The Portable Harlem Renaissance Reader*, Viking Penguin

Time-Life Books. *The Home Front: U.S.A.* (Depression and World War II)

Time-Life Books. *This Fabulous Century* (1 volume per decade)

Vogel, Virgil J., ed. *This Country Was Ours: A Documentary History of the American Indian*

Wright, Richard. *Black Boy*

## Collections of Primary Source Documents: Print

*The Annals of America.* Chicago: Encyclopedia Britannica, 1968.

Commager, Henry Steele, ed. *Documents of American History.* 9th ed. 2 vols. Englewood Cliffs, NJ: Prentice-Hall, 1973.

Craven, Avery, Walter Johnson, and F. Roger Dunn. *A Documentary History of the American People.* Boston: Ginn and Company, 1951.

Hart, Albert Bushnell, ed. *American History Told by Contemporaries, Vol. 5: Twentieth Century United States.* New York: The Macmillan Company, 1929.

*Historical Statistics of the United States.* Washington, DC: U.S. Department of Commerce, Bureau of the Census, 1975.

Miller, Marion Mills, ed. *Great Debates in American History.* 14 volumes in all. New York: Current Literature Publishing Company, 1913.

## CD-ROM

*America Adventure.* Knowledge Adventure.

*American Indian 2.0.* Facts on File.

*American Journey—History in Your Hands.* Research Publications.
*The African-American Experience*
*The Asian-American Experience*
*The Great Depression & the New Deal*
*The Hispanic-American Experience*
*Immigrant Experience in America*
*The Native-American Experience*
*Women in America*
*World War I and the Jazz Age*

*The American Multimedia Archive: The Complete Collection.* Facts on File.

*CD Sourcebook of American History.* InfoBases.

*FDR: Franklin Delano Roosevelt.* Corbis.

*500 Nations.* Microsoft.

*The Grapes of Wrath.* Penguin.

*The Great Depression.* Clearvue.

*The History of the United States for Young People.* American Heritage.

*Landmark Documents in American History.* Facts on File.

*Voices of the 30s.* Sunburst/Wings for Learning.

## World Wide Web/Internet

*Sites with numerous links to U.S. history sources are listed below. Sites of more specific interest are listed where appropriate in the Answers and Additional Activity sections above.*

The American Experience (PBS) (lists a variety of interesting sites based on PBS programs, including Nellie Bly, teenage hoboes, forgotten inventors, and more):
http://www.pbs.org/wgbh/amex/index.html

AMDOCS: Documents for the Study of American History (primary documents in full text):
http://www.mnu.edu/us_docs/

The Avalon Project at the Yale Law School (a large collection of historical documents):
http://www.yale.edu/awweb/avalon/avalon.htm

History/Social Studies Web Site for K–12 Teachers (includes site map, What's New Archive, sources arranged by category):
http://www.execpc.com/~dboals/boals.html

Kathy Schrock's Guide for Educators (a Cape Cod teacher's excellent list of resources):
http://school.discovery.com/schrockguide

Library of Congress American Memory (variety of fascinating historical collections):
http://memory.loc.gov/ammem/amhome.html

Library of Congress home page (special collections, historical documents, and more):
http://lcweb.loc.gov

# GLOSSARY

**armistice**—an agreement to end fighting; a truce.

**depression**—a downturn in economic activity.

**Dust Bowl**—the portion of the Great Plains that was engulfed by dust storms during the 1930s.

**espionage**—the act of spying.

**flapper**—a thoroughly modern 1920s young woman.

**fundamentalism**—adherence to traditional religious beliefs.

**ghetto**—section of a city where members of a minority group live, especially because social and economic pressures force them to be there.

**immigration**—nonnative people (**immigrants**) coming into a foreign country intending to live there permanently.

**labor union**—an organization of workers.

**lynching**—putting a person to death by mob action without due process of law.

**minimum wage**—the lowest hourly wage an employer can pay employees, by law.

**muckraker**—a Progressive reformer who wrote about aspects of American society that needed to be reformed.

**nativist**—a person who opposes immigration into his or her country.

**neutral**—not being allied with either opposing side in a war.

**New Deal**—the program to combat the Great Depression in the 1930s.

**Progressive movement**—reform movement of the 1900s and 1910s.

**Prohibition**—a ban on the manufacture and sale of alcoholic beverages in the United States, made the law of the land by the Eighteenth Amendment to the U.S. Constitution and repealed by the Twenty-First Amendment.

**propaganda**—the spreading of ideas or information to help promote a cause.

**quota**—a share or proportion assigned to members of a group.

**reparations**—payments for damages.

**rural**—referring to the country and country life.

**sedition**—promoting resistance to or rebellion against lawful authority.

**sharecropper**—person who farms another person's land and gives the landowner a share of the crop in payment.

**stock market**—place where people buy and sell shares (stock) in corporations.

**strike**—to stop work in order to force an employer to agree to workers' demands; also, the act of striking.

**tariff**—a set of taxes on goods brought into one country from another country.

**tenant farmer**—person who rents the land she or he farms from the landowner.

**treaty**—a formal agreement between two (or more) nations.

**U-boat**—German term for a submarine (*Unterseeboot*).

**unemployment**—the condition of being out of a job and unable to find one.

**urban**—having to do with the city and city life.

**woman suffrage**—the right of women to vote in local, state, and national elections.

# Notes

# Notes

# Share Your Bright Ideas

## We want to hear from you!

Your name_____Date_____

School name_____

School address_____

City _____State _____Zip_____Phone number (_____)_____

Grade level(s) taught_____Subject area(s) taught_____

Where did you purchase this publication?_____

In what month do you purchase a majority of your supplements?_____

What moneys were used to purchase this product?

_____School supplemental budget        _____Federal/state funding        _____Personal

### Please "grade" this Walch publication in the following areas:

| | A | B | C | D |
|---|---|---|---|---|
| Quality of service you received when purchasing | A | B | C | D |
| Ease of use | A | B | C | D |
| Quality of content | A | B | C | D |
| Page layout | A | B | C | D |
| Organization of material | A | B | C | D |
| Suitability for grade level | A | B | C | D |
| Instructional value | A | B | C | D |

COMMENTS:_____

_____

What specific supplemental materials would help you meet your current—or future—instructional needs?

_____

Have you used other Walch publications? If so, which ones?_____

May we use your comments in upcoming communications?      _____Yes      _____No

Please **FAX** this completed form to **888-991-5755**, or mail it to

### Customer Service, Walch Publishing, P. O. Box 658, Portland, ME 04104-0658

We will send you a **FREE GIFT** in appreciation of your feedback.  **THANK YOU!**